3

MASTERS AND WORKSHEETS

WATERFORD EARLY READING PROGRAM™

LEVEL TWO

Contents

CUTOUTS

CHECK SHEETS

WORKSHEETS

NEWSLETTERS

CUTOUTS

POWER WORD CARDS

it

on

the

a

is

me

what

• Introductory Lessons / Lesson B

I

• Unit 1 / Lesson 1

he

• Unit 1 / Lesson 3

in

• Introductory Lessons / Lesson B

see

• Unit 1 / Lesson 3

said

• Unit 1 / Lesson 4

are

my

go

says

have

will

his

• Unit 2 / Lesson 7

for

• Unit 2 / Lesson 8

with

• Unit 2 / Lesson 9

has

• Unit 2 / Lesson 7

you

• Unit 2 / Lesson 8

here

• Unit 2 / Lesson 9

to

put

she

of

be

they

her

who

let

from

come

your

too

no

look

we

yes

now

down

then

that

went

get

by

so

why

mother

little

like

do

father

Unit 4 / Lesson 20

Mr.

Unit 4 / Lesson 20

far

Unit 5 / Lesson 21

want

Unit 4 / Lesson 20

was

Unit 5 / Lesson 21

fall

Unit 5 / Lesson 21

out

find

friend

day

or

one

new

some

house

tree

thank

good

all

play

sure

how

does

were

could

many

walk

their

love

hold

cold

ears

where

pull

eyes

would

over

room

small

read

please

any

because

• Unit 7 / Lesson 33

tomorrow

• Unit 8 / Lesson 34

two

• Unit 8 / Lesson 35

door

• Unit 7 / Lesson 33

live

• Unit 7 / Lesson 33

buy

• Unit 8 / Lesson 34

start

don't

never

school

under

eat

there

• Unit 8 / Lesson 37

around

• Unit 9 / Lesson 38

very

• Unit 9 / Lesson 39

• Unit 8 / Lesson 37

our

• Unit 8 / Lesson 37

know

• Unit 9 / Lesson 38

think

old

every

saw

work

way

began

show

only

other

better

push

wait

thought

• Unit 10 / Lesson 44

soon

• Unit 10 / Lesson 44

after

• Unit 10 / Lesson 44

laugh

• Unit 10 / Lesson 45

both

• Unit 10 / Lesson 45

CUTOUTS

LETTER CARDS

NOTE: You may want to copy the letter cards double-sided so that you can use either the capital letter or the lowercase letter quickly by flipping the card over.

D

R

B

S

C

P

M

T

N

a

• Unit 1 / Lesson 2

r

• Unit 1 / Lesson 4

b

• Unit 2 / Lesson 7

s

• Unit 1 / Lesson 1

c

• Unit 1 / Lesson 3

d

• Unit 1 / Lesson 5

m

• Unit 1 / Lesson 1

t

• Unit 1 / Lesson 3

n

• Unit 1 / Lesson 4

G

• Unit 2 / Lesson 9

K

• Unit 3 / Lesson 13

Z

• Unit 4 / Lesson 18

X

• Unit 2 / Lesson 8

L

• Unit 3 / Lesson 12

Y

• Unit 4 / Lesson 17

F

• Unit 2 / Lesson 8

H

• Unit 3 / Lesson 11

J

• Unit 3 / Lesson 14

g

• Unit 2 / Lesson 9

k

• Unit 3 / Lesson 13

N

• Unit 4 / Lesson 18

x

• Unit 2 / Lesson 8

l

• Unit 3 / Lesson 12

Y

• Unit 4 / Lesson 17

f

• Unit 2 / Lesson 8

n

• Unit 3 / Lesson 11

j

• Unit 3 / Lesson 14

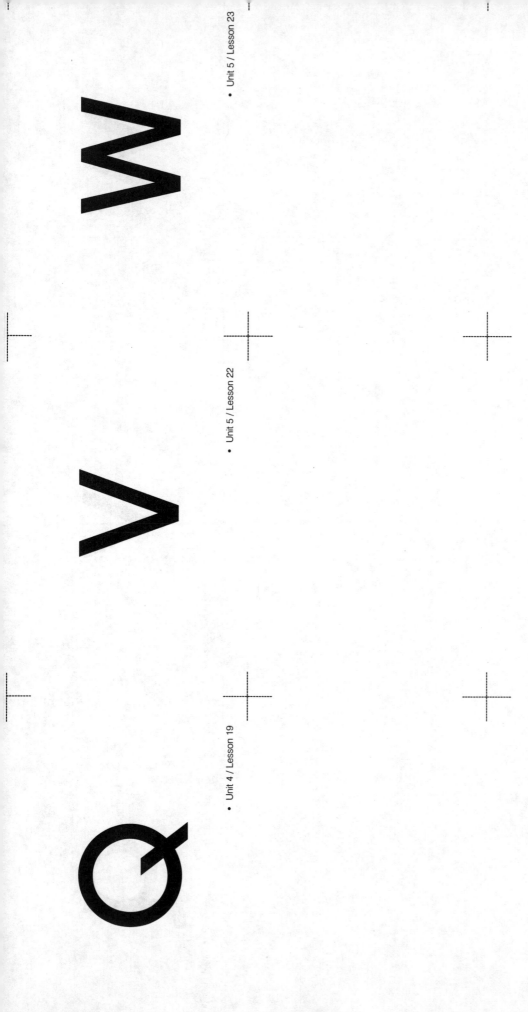

• Unit 5 / Lesson 23

• Unit 5 / Lesson 22

• Unit 4 / Lesson 19

W

V

p

I

• Unit 3 / Lesson 10

O

• Unit 2 / Lesson 6

E

• Unit 5 / Lesson 21

A

• Unit 1 / Lesson 1

U

• Unit 4 / Lesson 16

i

• Unit 3 / Lesson 10

e

O

• Unit 5 / Lesson 21

• Unit 2 / Lesson 6

u

a

• Unit 4 / Lesson 16

• Unit 1 / Lesson 1

CUTOUTS

BLEND AND DIGRAPH CARDS

sc • Unit 1 / Lesson 3	nt • Unit 1 / Lesson 4	nd • Unit 1 / Lesson 4
mp • Unit 1 / Lesson 5	st • Unit 2 / Lesson 6	sn • Unit 2 / Lesson 7
cr • Unit 2 / Lesson 7	fr • Unit 2 / Lesson 9	sm • Unit 2 / Unit Review

tr

• Unit 3 / Lesson 10

gr

• Unit 3 / Lesson 11

fl

• Unit 3 / Lesson 12

pr

• Unit 3 / Lesson 12

cl

• Unit 3 / Lesson 12

lk

• Unit 3 / Lesson 13

sk

• Unit 3 / Lesson 13

ck

• Unit 3 / Lesson 14

sh

• Unit 3 / Lesson 15

br

qu

tch

sl

dr

ch

spl

scr

th

wh

SECTION D

CUTOUTS

WORD PATTERN CARDS

ad

an

ant

am

at

and

op

pd

ap

qo

ot

amp

oss

ax

ag

ab

ox

ag

ip

in

id

ig

im

it

.int

ack

.ick

.ill

.ing

ock

ash

ug

ut

ish

un

um

ush

izz

uff

ub

uzz

uck

ump

• Unit 4 / Lesson 19

ell

• Unit 5 / Lesson 21

en

• Unit 5 / Lesson 21

ed

• Unit 5 / Lesson 21

est

• Unit 5 / Lesson 21

et

• Unit 5 / Lesson 21

ent

ade

ame

end

y

ake

ane

ave

ace

ate

are

age

ose

ole

ode

ope

oke

one

ote

• Unit 7 / Lesson 32

ove

• Unit 7 / Lesson 33

ime

• Unit 8 / Lesson 34

ore

• Unit 7 / Lesson 33

ide

• Unit 8 / Lesson 34

ime

• Unit 8 / Lesson 35

ice

ile

ike

ite

ire

ive

ipe

ute

ude

ube

ule

une

eep

eet

eal

use

eed

eak

eam

• Unit 10 / Lesson 43

ain

• Unit 10 / Lesson 44

oat

• Unit 10 / Lesson 45

ail

• Unit 10 / Lesson 44

ay

• Unit 10 / Lesson 44

oad

• Unit 10 / Lesson 45

CUTOUTS

KEY WORD CARDS

• Unit 1 / Lesson 2

mad

• Unit 1 / Lesson 4

can

• Unit 1 / Lesson 5

map

• Unit 1 / Lesson 1

Sam

• Unit 1 / Lesson 3

cat

• Unit 1 / Lesson 4

sand

stamp

• Unit 1 / Lesson 5

pot

• Unit 2 / Lesson 6

cob

• Unit 2 / Lesson 7

rod

• Unit 2 / Lesson 6

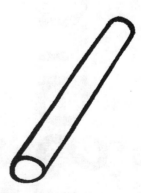

stop

• Unit 2 / Lesson 6

crab

• Unit 2 / Lesson 7

frog

• Unit 2 / Lesson 9

rip

• Unit 3 / Lesson 10

pin

• Unit 3 / Lesson 10

box

• Unit 2 / Lesson 8

bag

• Unit 2 / Lesson 9

pig

• Unit 3 / Lesson 10

swim

• Unit 3 / Lesson 11

pit

• Unit 3 / Lesson 11

print

• Unit 3 / Lesson 12

lid

• Unit 3 / Lesson 11

hill

• Unit 3 / Lesson 12

king

• Unit 3 / Lesson 13

clock

• Unit 3 / Lesson 14

trash

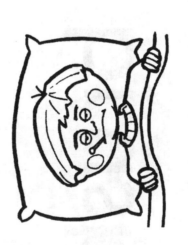

• Unit 3 / Lesson 15

sun

• Unit 4 / Lesson 16

black

• Unit 3 / Lesson 14

sick

• Unit 3 / Lesson 14

bug

• Unit 4 / Lesson 16

nut

tub

fizz

drum

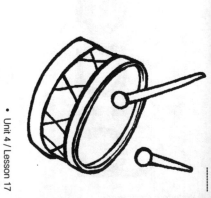

brush

truck

pump

sled

nest

cuff

thing

shell

ten

10

net

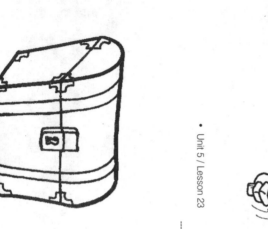

bend

tent

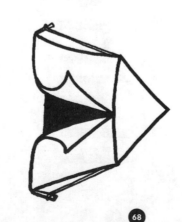

chest

fly

68

snake

plane

wave

spade

game

skate

square

rope

stone

lace

smoke

store

dime

mice

flute

slide

vine

hive

cube

• Unit 9 / Lesson 39

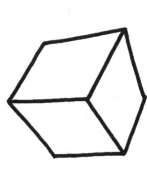

dune

• Unit 9 / Lesson 40

skated

• Unit 9 / Lesson 41

jeep

• Unit 10 / Lesson 42

seed

• Unit 10 / Lesson 42

street

• Unit 10 / Lesson 42

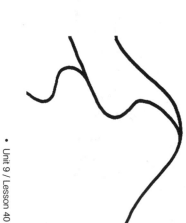

72

seal

snail

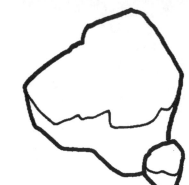

clay

beak

cream

chain

goat

• Unit 10 / Lesson 45

SECTION F

CUTOUTS

SENTENCE STRIPS

I am Sam.

What am I?

I am Dad.

What is it, Dad?

Tad is a cat.

See Matt's hat on

Dad.

Ann sat in the sand.

Mac is on the stand.

Pam can stamp!

Can Pat see the

camp?

I cannot stop the

frogs.

Todd is a good cop.

"Ouch!" says Tab.

Bob says, "I can't see

the crabs."

"I have a box for

you," says Rox.

Max's hot rod is off!

"What is in the bag?"

says Fran Frog.

"It is a surprise!" says

Top Dog.

Pip is a big pig.

A cap and a map go

in the jeep.

They will see what is

in the pit.

Tim grabs his hat and

puts it on.

Bill sees a hill.

The prints on the

Unit 3 / Readable 12

hilltop are from her

Unit 3 / Readable 12

cans.

Unit 3 / Readable 12

© Waterford Institute

88

"Can I see the cat?"

says Todd.

She is bringing the

milk.

"We are going on a

trip to Grandma's,"

says Mom.

Mac fills his

backpack.

Who will go in the

rain?

The fish flips and flops

in the pond.

I see a big bug on

the sun.

I see 5 bugs down in

the jug.

Josh got gum on the

rug.

Then he got gum on

his dog, Gus.

I'm Lizzy the fuzzy little bee.

I will go buzzing by

Tabby the cat.

I can't jump like a bunny.

Little Duck said,

"Quack! Quack! Quack!

Quack!""

Kath did her math.

"I want you to see a

monster!" said Kath.

99

They will test the

sleds at the park.

Let's go back to the

little hill.

Meg sees the egg

jump.

A bill pops out of the

egg!

Rom can go with his

mother and father to

the camp.

You are my best

friend!

Chet Chimp is

hanging from his

branch.

His house shakes

when Chet scratches.

He does tricks in the

sky.

How do I spy a fly, a

fox, a pig, a crab,

and a cat?

He wants to have

cake and lemonade.

Rex and Sal were in

the mud this morning.

Dane is going to see

Grandma and

Grandpa.

Dane skates on the

sidewalk by the

house.

Dave is holding on to

the wing.

Look out for that tree!

My snowman stands

by the house.

He is cold, but he is

happy.

Mose just fell down

the slope!

I can see him by that

rose.

"Oh no, I smell

smoke!" said the

small mole.

It's the smoke from

their grill!

"The note is in code,"

says Max.

Come home for an

ice cream cone.

It is a chore to live

next door to a boar

that snores.

I will not snore any

more.

They can sit side by

side in the wide

swing.

Jess can buy an ice

cream cone for a

dime.

Two little pines stand

side by side.

They stand in a line

by the school.

It is just what mice

like to eat.

A wire holds it to the

tree.

We are going on a

trip to Yellowstone.

We will stay for five

days.

She can play the flute

and skip around her

room.

Brute wants to take

his nap.

126

Old Rosa is a mule.

She's very old, but

she can do a lot of

work.

Every day June fixes

trees.

She must prune

every branch.

They skated over to

the school.

They played hide

and seek.

My little jeep goes

when I push my feet.

You can ride in my

jeep.

Sammmy is a

brand-new seal.

Pete pokes his beak

around the rock.

The little snail saw a

trail.

"Snails love to play in

the rain!" yelled

another.

One day two best

friends, Goat and

Toad, went for a walk.

He swam to a floating

oar and gave it to

Goat.

SeCtIoN G

CUTOUTS

GAME MARKERS

Leap Frog Game Marker

Directions: Make six copies of the frog marker master out of construction paper or card stock, each a different color. Use these markers for the game suggested in Unit Review 1 and Unit Review 6 of Book 3: *Learning to Read*.

Duck Pond Game Markers

Directions: Make five copies of the duck markers master out of *each* of the following colors of cardstock: yellow, orange, brown, green, and gray. Use these markers for the game suggested in Unit Review 1 and Unit Review 6 of Book 3: *Learning to Read.*

Ape

Directions: Make enough copies of the ape master to match the number of previously learned Power Words. Use the apes for the game suggested in Unit Review 5 and Unit Review 10 of Book 3: *Learning to Read.*

CHECK SHEETS

Unit Check Sheets: Student Copy

Introductory Lesson Check

A   in
I   the
me   what
is   it
on   a

It is on me.

What is in it?

Unit 1 Check

Sam	are
mad	what
cat	says
can	have
map	said

Can I see the stamps?

He can have my sand.

Unit 2 Check

pot

cob

for

bag

frog

go

has

you

with

box

Rod's crab will stop here.

His frogs are in the boxes.

Unit 3 Check

rip	of
pin	to
lid	who
print	yes
clock	no

She put your pig on the hill.

The trash comes from the black pit.

They will swim with the king.

We will not let her get sick, too!

Unit 4 Check

sun   now

nut   look

tub   down

cuff   then

pump   so

thrush

The little bug went to see his mother and father.

Why do you like drums and trucks?

I want to get a brush for Mr. Fizz.

Unit 5 Check

nest   fall

ten   day

bend   or

chest   one

far

My friend was out on his new sled.

That tent will be a good house.

Thank you for finding some shells.

How does a fish fly?

Unit 6 Check

spade   their

game   walk

square   pull

lace   were

play   ears

I love to skate in the cold.

Are you sure you could hold the

snake?

A snake has eyes but no legs.

Many of us wave to the plane.

Unit 7 Check

rope	small
nose	any
stone	door
stove	because
room	over

Please read me the note that is in code.

I smell smoke at the store.

Where will you live, Mr. Mole?

Unit 8 Check

slide	stripe
dime	don't
vine	under
kite	our
hive	there

Tomorrow the two mice will start school.

I know he will never eat that pile of rice.

My dad will buy a new tire for my bike.

Unit 9 Check

flute   think

cube   work

dune   way

use   saw

rude   better

Brute was a very old mule.

June began to play a tune on her flute.

He sang while he skated around.

Unit 10 Check

seed	show
beak	only
seal	wait
chain	laugh
clay	after

Both the toad and the frog liked the cream.

The goat thought he could push the jeep up the street.

Soon the other snail wanted to play.

CHECK SHEETS

UNIT CHECK SHEETS: TEACHER COPY

Child's Name: _____

Introductory Lessons Check

Instruct the student to read these words and sentences aloud. Make note of errors and comment below if necessary.

A

I

me

is

on

in

the

what

it

a

It is on me.

What is in it?

TOTAL NUMBER OF WORDS: 18   **NUMBER CORRECT:**

Comments:

• Teacher's Copy

Unit 1 Check

Instruct the student to read these words and sentences aloud. Make note of errors and comment below if necessary.

Sam	are
mad	what
cat	says
can	have
map	said

Can I see the stamps?

He can have my sand.

TOTAL NUMBER OF WORDS: 20   **NUMBER CORRECT:**

Comments:

• Teacher's Copy

Unit 2 Check

Instruct the student to read these words and sentences aloud. Make note of errors and comment below if necessary.

pot	go
cob	has
for	you
bag	with
frog	box

Rod's crab will stop here.

His frogs are in the boxes.

TOTAL NUMBER OF WORDS: 21   **NUMBER CORRECT:**

Comments:

Unit 3 Check

Instruct the student to read these words and sentences aloud. Make note of errors and comment below if necessary.

rip	of
pin	to
lid	who
print	yes
clock	no

She put your pig on the hill.

The trash comes from the black pit.

They will swim with the king.

We will not let her get sick, too!

TOTAL NUMBER OF WORDS: 38   **NUMBER CORRECT:**

Comments:

Unit 4 Check

Instruct the student to read these words and sentences aloud. Make note of errors and comment below if necessary.

sun   now

nut   look

tub   down

cuff   then

pump   so

thrush

The little bug went to see his mother and father.

Why do you like drums and trucks?

I want to get a brush for Mr. Fizz.

TOTAL NUMBER OF WORDS: 37   **NUMBER CORRECT:**

Comments:

Unit 5 Check

Instruct the student to read these words and sentences aloud. Make note of errors and comment below if necessary.

nest	fall
ten	day
bend	or
chest	one
far	

My friend was out on his new sled.

That tent will be a good house.

Thank you for finding some shells.

How does a fish fly?

TOTAL NUMBER OF WORDS: 35   **NUMBER CORRECT:**

Comments:

Unit 6 Check

Instruct the student to read these words and sentences aloud. Make note of errors and comment below if necessary.

spade	their
game	walk
square	pull
lace	were
play	ears

I love to skate in the cold.

Are you sure you could hold the snake?

A snake has eyes but no legs.

Many of us wave to the plane.

TOTAL NUMBER OF WORDS: 39   **NUMBER CORRECT:**

Comments:

• Teacher's Copy

Unit 7 Check

Instruct the student to read these words and sentences aloud. Make note of errors and comment below if necessary.

rope	small
nose	any
stone	door
stove	because
room	over

Please read me the note that is in code

I smell smoke at the store.

Where will you live, Mr. Mole?

TOTAL NUMBER OF WORDS: 31   **NUMBER CORRECT:**

Comments:

Unit 8 Check

Instruct the student to read these words and sentences aloud. Make note of errors and comment below if necessary.

slide   stripe

dime   don't

vine   under

kite   our

hive   there

Tomorrow the two mice will start school.

I know he will never eat that pile of rice.

My dad will buy a new tire for my bike.

TOTAL NUMBER OF WORDS: 37   **NUMBER CORRECT:**

Comments:

• Teacher's Copy

Unit 9 Check

Instruct the student to read these words and sentences aloud. Make note of errors and comment below if necessary.

flute   think

cube   work

dune   way

use   saw

rude   better

Brute was a very old mule.

June began to play a tune on her flute.

He sang while he skated around.

TOTAL NUMBER OF WORDS: 31   **NUMBER CORRECT:**

Comments:

• Teacher's Copy

Unit 10 Check

Instruct the student to read these words and sentences aloud. Make note of errors and comment below if necessary.

seed	show
beak	only
seal	wait
chain	laugh
clay	after

Both the toad and the frog liked the cream.

The goat thought he could push the jeep up the street.

Soon the other snail wanted to play.

TOTAL NUMBER OF WORDS: 37   **NUMBER CORRECT:**

Comments:

CHECK SHEETS

RECORDING CHECK SHEETS

Check the student's reading accuracy in the books recorded in the **Teacher Options** or read aloud in the classroom.

Me

(Power Word Readable A)

It is on a monkey.

It is on a giraffe.

It is on a lion.

It is on a kangaroo.

It is on a zebra.

It is on a camel.

It is on me.

TOTAL NUMBER OF WORDS: 34

Comments:

Check the student's reading accuracy in the books recorded in the **Teacher Options** or read aloud in the classroom.

The Snowman

(Power Word Readable B)

A snowman.

A coat is on the snowman.

A scarf is on the snowman.

A hat is on the snowman.

A flower is on the snowman.

A carrot is on the snowman.

A smile.

TOTAL NUMBER OF WORDS: 34

Comments:

Check the student's reading accuracy in the books recorded in the **Teacher Options** or read aloud in the classroom.

The Mitten

(Power Word Readable C)

What is in the mitten?

A mouse is in the mitten.

What is in the mitten?

A skunk is in the mitten.

What is in the mitten?

A porcupine is in the mitten.

What is in the mitten?

A bear is in the mitten.

POP!

TOTAL NUMBER OF WORDS: 45

Comments:

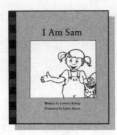

Check the student's reading accuracy in the books recorded in the **Teacher Options** or read aloud in the classroom.

I Am Sam

(Readable 1A)

I am Sam.

I am on a pig.

I am on a dragon.

I am on a fish.

I am in a cup.

I am on a horse.

I am on a merry-go-round!

TOTAL NUMBER OF WORDS: 33

Comments:

Check the student's reading accuracy in the books recorded in the **Teacher Options** or read aloud in the classroom.

What Am I?

(Readable 1B)

What am I?

I am a green frog.

What am I?

I am a pink pig.

What am I?

I am a red bird.

What am I?

I am a brown bear.

What am I?

I am a blue fish.

What am I?

I am me!

TOTAL NUMBER OF WORDS: 46

Comments:

Check the student's reading accuracy in the books recorded in the **Teacher Options** or read aloud in the classroom.

Sad Sam

(Readable 2A)

I am Sam.

I am Dad.

Sam is sad.

Dad! Dad! What is it, Dad?

A nail is in it. Dad is mad.

Dad is at the shop.

Sam is happy.

Dad is happy.

TOTAL NUMBER OF WORDS: 34

Comments:

Check the student's reading accuracy in the books recorded in the **Teacher Options** or read aloud in the classroom.

Dad's Surprise

(Readable 2B)

Dad is in a tree.

The boards.

The saw.

The nails. The hammer.

Sam! Sam!

What is it, Dad?

Surprise!

I am in the tree house.

TOTAL NUMBER OF WORDS: 26

Comments:

Child's Name: _____

Check the student's reading accuracy in the books recorded in the **Teacher Options** or read aloud in the classroom.

Tad

(Readable 3A)

Tad is a cat.

He sat on a mat.

Tad! See the box!

Is a bird in the box?

Is a dog in the box?

Is a mouse in the box?

Tad is on the box.

Tad is in the box.

Tad sees...

Me! I am in the box.

TOTAL NUMBER OF WORDS: 49

Comments:

Check the student's reading accuracy in the books recorded in the **Teacher Options** or read aloud in the classroom.

Matt's Hat

(Readable 3B)

Matt's hat.

See Matt's hat on Mom.

See Matt's hat on Dad.

Matt's hat is on the baby.

Matt's hat is on the mat.

A cat sat on Matt's hat. Scat, cat, scat!

Matt's hat is on Matt.

TOTAL NUMBER OF WORDS: 38

Comments:

Check the student's reading accuracy in the books recorded in the **Teacher Options** or read aloud in the classroom.

What Is It?

(Readable 4A)

Ann sat in the sand.

The ants ran. "What is it?" said Ann.

The cats ran. "What is it?" said Ann.

A man ran in the sand. "What is it?" said Ann.

"Is it a bear?"

"Is it a dragon?"

"Is it a monster?"

"I can see it!" said Ann.

Ann ran.

What is it?

Rain!

TOTAL NUMBER OF WORDS: 56

Comments:

Check the student's reading accuracy in the books recorded in the **Teacher Options** or read aloud in the classroom.

Dan and Mac

(Readable 4B)

See Dan and Mac.

Dan is on the sand. Mac is on the stand.

Dan and Mac are in the band.

See Dan stand on hands.

Dan and Mac are on a man.

"Mac! Mac! Dan! Dan! I can't stand," says the man.

Aaaaaaaaaaaaaaaaaaaaaaaa!

Mac, Dan, and the man are in the sand.

TOTAL NUMBER OF WORDS: 53

Comments:

• Unit 1 / Lesson 4B

Check the student's reading accuracy in the books recorded in the **Teacher Options** or read aloud in the classroom.

What a Band!

(Readable 5A)

Pam and Andy have a band.

See Pam and a can.

Tap! Tap! Tap!

See Andy and a pan.

Rat-a-tat! Rat-a-tat!

See Ann. Ann is sad.

"Have the can," says Pam.

Ann can tap. Tap! Tap! Tap!

Andy can rat-a-tat. Rat-a-tat!

Pam can stamp! Stamp! Stamp! Stamp!

What a fun band!

TOTAL NUMBER OF WORDS: 51

Comments:

Check the student's reading accuracy in the books recorded in the **Teacher Options** or read aloud in the classroom.

Pat Can Camp

(Readable 5B)

Pat can camp.

"I have my tan tent and my mat," says Pat.

He can see the camp on the map.

Pat is on a trail.

He is on a bridge.

He is in a stream.

Can Pat see the camp?

He can!

"My mat is in the tent," says Pat.

"I can have a nap." Good night!

TOTAL NUMBER OF WORDS: 58

Comments:

Check the student's reading accuracy in the books recorded in the **Teacher Options** or read aloud in the classroom.

The Rabbit and the Turtle

(Review Readable 1)

Chapter 1

The rabbit and the turtle ran.

The rabbit ran past the turtle.

He ran past the cat.

He ran past the sand.

The rabbit ran and ran.

The rabbit sat. "I can nap," he said.

Chapter 2

See the turtle.

He can pass the cat and the sand.

He can pass the rabbit.

The turtle pants and pants.

He is at the camp!

The rabbit sees the turtle. What a sad rabbit!

What a happy turtle!

TOTAL NUMBER OF WORDS: 74

Comments:

Check the student's reading accuracy in the books recorded in the **Teacher Options** or read aloud in the classroom.

Stop the Frogs!

(Readable 6)

Stop! Stop! Stop the frogs!

Todd is a good cop. "I will stop the frogs."

"Stop, frogs! Stop!"

The frogs will not stop.

"I cannot stop the frogs."

Todd will stop the car. He will stop the truck.

Todd will stop the bus. He will stop the bike.

The frogs can go.

The frogs are in the pond. Todd is happy.

TOTAL NUMBER OF WORDS: 61

Comments:

Check the student's reading accuracy in the books recorded in the **Teacher Options** or read aloud in the classroom.

Bob and Tab

(Readable 7)

Bob and Tab are in a cab. Bob and Tab are at the sea.

Tab sees a crab in the sand. Bob sees a crab in the moss.

Snap! Snap! Tab has a crab on his nose.

"Ouch!" says Tab.

Snap! Snap! Bob has a crab on his toe.

"Ouch!" says Bob.

Bob and Tab go in the cab. Bob and Tab sob and sob.

Bob says, "I can't see the crabs."

"Good-bye, crabs."

TOTAL NUMBER OF WORDS: 75

Comments:

Check the student's reading accuracy in the books recorded in the **Teacher Options** or read aloud in the classroom.

Hot Rods

(Readable 8)

Rox Fox has a hot rod.

Rox can go fast.

Rox has a box for Max. "I have a box for you," says Rox.

A hot rod for Max.

Rox has a box for Sam. "I have a box for you," says Rox.

A hot rod for Sam.

1, 2, 3 boxes. 1, 2, 3 foxes.

1, 2, 3, GO!

Rox's hot rod is off! Max's hot rod is off! Sam's hot rod is off!

Off go the fast hot rods.

TOTAL NUMBER OF WORDS: 81

Comments:

Check the student's reading accuracy in the books recorded in the **Teacher Options** or read aloud in the classroom.

Happy Birthday

(Readable 9)

Bob Frog has a bag with a tag. "What is in the bag?" says Fran Frog.

"It is a surprise!" says Bob Frog.

Top Dog has a bag with a tag. "What is in the bag?" says Fran Frog.

"It is a surprise!" says Top Dog.

Max Fox has a bag with a tag. "What is in the bag?" says Fran Frog.

"It is a surprise!" says Max Fox.

SURPRISE!

Here is a dress.

Here is a hat.

Here is an alligator purse!

"Happy Birthday, Fran Frog!"

TOTAL NUMBER OF WORDS: 87

Comments:

Check the student's reading accuracy in the books recorded in the **Teacher Options** or read aloud in the classroom.

Go, Frog, Go!

(Review Readable 2)

Frog ran in the fog. He ran in the smog. Go, Frog, go!

Frog ran with Mom. He ran with Tom. Go, Frog, go!

Frog ran with Ross. He ran with his boss. Go, Frog, go!

Frog ran with Bob. He ran with a mob. Go, Frog, go!

Frog ran with Don. He ran with Ron. Go, Frog, go!

Frog ran with a fox. He ran with an ox. Go, Frog, go!

Frog ran with a band. He ran in the sand. Go, Frog, go!

Frog can go fast. Will he go past? Stop, Frog! Stop!

TOTAL NUMBER OF WORDS: 96

Comments:

Check the student's reading accuracy in the books recorded in the **Teacher Options** or read aloud in the classroom.

Pip, the Big Pig

(Readable 10)

Pip is a big pig. "I will go on a trip to the beach," says Pip.

"I can go in my jeep. It will be fun!"

"Rig-a-dig-dig, rig-a-dig-dig. What can fit in my jeep?"

A cap and a mat go in the jeep.

A mask and fins go in.

Pip has a box of balls. Pip has a box of food.

"Rig-a-dig-dig, rig-a-dig-dig. See what is in the jeep!"

Can Pip go in?

He can!

Pop, pop, pop! Off you go, Pip!

Pip, the pig, is at the beach.

TOTAL NUMBER OF WORDS: 89

Comments:

Check the student's reading accuracy in the books recorded in the **Teacher Options** or read aloud in the classroom.

What Is in the Pit?

(Readable 11)

Tim and Sid see a pit. What is in the pit?

Is it a snake?

Is it a rabbit?

Tim and Sid are in the grass. They will see what is in the pit. They sit and sit.

It is hot. Tim puts his hat on the grass. He has a nap.

Hiss! Hiss! Hiss! "What is it?" says Sid.

Tim grabs his hat and puts it on.

"What's in my hat?" says Tim. "Is it a snake?" says Sid. "Did it go in the hat?"

It did! Hiss! Hiss! Hiss!

Tim puts the snake in the grass.

Off goes the snake! Go, snake! Go!

TOTAL NUMBER OF WORDS: 105

Comments:

Check the student's reading accuracy in the books recorded in the **Teacher Options** or read aloud in the classroom.

Prints!

(Readable 12)

Bill sees a hill.

He sees prints on the hilltop.

Are they dinosaur prints?

Bill goes to the hill.

Clomp, clomp, clomp! What is it? Is it a dinosaur?

Bill is in a box. He sits still.

Clomp, clomp, clomp!

Bill sees Mika!

She has cans on her feet. The prints on the hilltop are from her cans.

"Here are cans for you," Mika says.

Off they go! Clomp, clomp, clomp!

TOTAL NUMBER OF WORDS: 71

Comments:

Child's Name:_____

Check the student's reading accuracy in the books recorded in the **Teacher Options** or read aloud in the classroom.

Who Is at the Door?

(Readable 13)

Ding-dong! Who is at the door? Is it Dad?

It's Todd. "Can I see the cat?" says Todd. "Come in!"

Todd pats the soft cat. She is napping in her box.

Ding-dong! Who is at the door? Is it Dad?

It's Kim. She is bringing the milk. "Come in!"

Ding-dong! Who is at the door? Is it Dad?

It's Alan. He has come to fix the oven. "Come in!"

Ding-dong! Who is at the door? Is it Dad?

It is! He has the pizza. "Come in!"

"Let's eat!"

TOTAL NUMBER OF WORDS: 92

Comments:

• Unit 3 / Lesson 13

Check the student's reading accuracy in the books recorded in the **Teacher Options** or read aloud in the classroom.

The Big Trip

(Readable 14)

"We are going on a trip to Grandma's," says Mom. "We are going on the train."

"We will see Sid and Nick, too," says Jill. "Go pack your backpacks," says Mom.

Mack fills his backpack. He puts in socks and pants. He puts in a ball and a stick.

Jill puts an apple in her pack. She puts a lock on her pack.

Mom, Jill, and Mack are on the train. The train goes click-clack on the track.

The train stops. "Here we are!"

Mom sits with Grandma.

Mack has a ball and stick for Nick.

Jill has an apple for Sid.

What fun!

TOTAL NUMBER OF WORDS: 104

Comments:

Check the student's reading accuracy in the books recorded in the **Teacher Options** or read aloud in the classroom.

Who Will Go in the Rain?

(Readable 15)

Rain! Who will go in the rain?

Will a dog go in the rain?

Yes! A dog can splish and splash in the rain.

Will the fish go in the rain?

Yes! The fish flips and flops in the pond.

Will the cat go in the rain?

No! The cat is in the shed.

Will Nashota go in the rain?

Yes! Nashota puts her ship in the pond.

"Can I go in the rain?" "No!" says Mom. "If I have a hat and boots?"

"Yes!" she says. Splish-splash, splish-splash, splish-splash.

TOTAL NUMBER OF WORDS: 90

Comments:

Check the student's reading accuracy in the books recorded in the **Teacher Options** or read aloud in the classroom.

Let's Get Hats!

(Review Readable 3)

Jim and Trish go to the shop. They can get hats.

What hat will Jim get?

Here is a hat with a wig. Is it a hat for Jim? No!

Jim puts on a fishing hat. Jim, is it the hat for you? No!

Trish has a black hat for Jim. She puts it on him. Will it fit? Yes! I have my hat!

Trish, can you get a hat?

Trish puts on a hat. It is a stocking cap. Is it the hat for you, Trish? No!

Here is a trick hat. A rabbit can come out. Who will have the hat? Not Trish!

Here comes Jim with a hat for Trish. It is a big hat with a sash.

Trish puts it on. "I will have a big hat," says Trish.

"We love the hats!"

TOTAL NUMBER OF WORDS: 137

Comments:

Check the student's reading accuracy in the books recorded in the **Teacher Options** or read aloud in the classroom.

Slug Bug

(Readable 16)

I see a big bug on the sun. Slug Bug run! Slug Bug fun! I got you. Now I have 1.

I see a big bug on my shoe. Slug Bug run! Slug Bug fun! I got you. Now I have 2.

I see a big bug on the tree. Slug Bug run! Slug Bug fun! I got you. Now I have 3.

I see a big bug on my door. Slug Bug run! Slug Bug fun! I got you. Now I have 4.

I see a big bug on the hive. Slug Bug run! Slug Bug fun! I got you. Now I have 5.

I see 5 bugs down in the jug. The bugs look Slug Bug sad. The bugs look at me. But I'm not glad.

Slug Bug run! Slug Bug fun! Look at the Slug Bugs run, run, run.

OTAL NUMBER OF WORDS: 142

Comments:

Check the student's reading accuracy in the books recorded in the **Teacher Options** or read aloud in the classroom.

Green Gum

(Readable 17)

Josh had fun with his gum. "Yum! Yum! Green gum is fun!" said Josh.

Josh had to rush. He got gum in his mush. "Yum! Yum! Green gum is fun!" said Josh.

Josh got gum on the rug. He got gum on his bus. Then he got gum on his dog, Gus.

"Yum! Yum! Green gum is fun!" said Josh.

*Mom said, "Here are your soap and brush. Now go to the tub. Rub and scrub. Scrub and

rub. Get rid of that green gum!"

Josh went to the tub. Rubbing and scrubbing. Scrubbing and rubbing. He got rid of the

green gum.

But then he got gum on the tub.

"Oh no!" said Mom. "You still have gum!"

"Yup!" said Josh. "Yum! Yum! Green gum is fun!"

* The text on this line has been revised and may not match the text the student reads from. Please take this into account when scoring the student's reading accuracy.

TOTAL NUMBER OF WORDS: 128

Comments:

Check the student's reading accuracy in the books recorded in the **Teacher Options** or read aloud in the classroom.

Lizzy the Bee

(Readable 18)

"Hi! I'm Lizzy the fuzzy little bee."

"I can buzz. Buzzing is so fun."

"Can I buzz in the hive?" "Not in the hive!" Mom bee said.

"Buzzing is so fun," said Lizzy. "I will go buzzing by Bossy the cow."

Fuzzy Lizzy went buzzing by Bossy the cow.

"Not by the cow!" Mom bee said. "Bossy the cow will get dizzy!"

"Buzzing is so fun," said Lizzy. "I will go buzzing by Tabby the cat."

Fuzzy Lizzy went buzzing by Tabby the cat.

"Not by the cat!" Mom bee said. "Tabby the cat will get dizzy!"

"Buzzing is so fun," said Lizzy. "I will go buzzing by Snappy the flower."

Fuzzy Lizzy went buzzing by Snappy the flower.

"Yes, by the flower!" Mom bee said.

TOTAL NUMBER OF WORDS: 126

Comments:

Check the student's reading accuracy in the books recorded in the **Teacher Options** or read aloud in the classroom.

Little Duck

(Readable 19)

"Oh, Floppy Bunny! Can I be like you?" said Little Duck.

"Why not?" said Floppy Bunny. "Can you jump, jump, jump like me?"

But Little Duck's feet went flip-flop, flip-flop. "Oh my!" said Little Duck. "I can't jump like a bunny."

"Oh, Fluffy Hen! Can I be like you?" said Little Duck.

"Why not?" said Fluffy Hen. "Can you cluck, cluck, cluck like me?"

But Little Duck said, "Quack! Quack! Quack!" "Oh my!" said Little Duck. "I can't cluck like a hen."

"Then what can I do?"

"I can swim in a pond. A bunny can't swim in a pond."

"I can quack, quack, quack. A hen can't quack, quack, quack."

"I am what I am!" said Little Duck. "I am a duck!"

TOTAL NUMBER OF WORDS: 123

Comments:

Check the student's reading accuracy in the books recorded in the **Teacher Options** or read aloud in the classroom.

Thump, Bump!

(Readable 20)

Kath did her math. She had a bath. Then Kath went to bed.

Thump, bump! Thump, bump! "What is that?" said Kath.

Kath went to her father. "Come with me! I want you to see a monster!" said Kath.

"That is not a monster," said Father. "Please go back to bed!"

Thump, bump! Thump, bump! "What is that?" said Kath.

Kath went to her mother. "Come with me! I want you to see a dragon!" said Kath.

"That is not a dragon," said Mother. "Please go back to bed!"

Kath went back to bed. Thump, bump! Thump, bump! Thump, bump!

Kath went to the window. "Look, Mr. Tubbs wants to come in," said Kath. "He is thumping

and bumping on the window."

"Come in! Come in, Mr. Tubbs!" said Kath.

At last Kath and Mr. Tubbs went to bed.

TOTAL NUMBER OF WORDS: 139

Comments:

Check the student's reading accuracy in the books recorded in the **Teacher Options** or read aloud in the classroom.

The Tree Hut

(Review Readable 4)

I have a tree hut. The hut is by a pond. My dog, Lucky, wants to go with me.

To get to the tree hut, we go by a path. The bees hum and buzz in the trees. Lucky tugs as we run down the path.

At last, we get to the pond. Lucky and I jump in with a big splash.

We have lots of fun. Lucky likes me to rub and brush his back.

Then we go up into the tree hut. We go up and up the ladder.

Now we can look down at the pond. We see ducks quacking in the pond. Mother ducks go up and down looking for bugs.

A raccoon comes to the stump by the pond. She is so funny as she fishes for lunch.

Now and then, deer stand by the pond and look. The deer are quick. They rush back to the trees.

My father comes down the path looking for us. He looks for us up in the tree hut.

"Good-bye tree hut," I say. "Ruff, ruff," says Lucky.

"We will be back," I say to my tree hut.

TOTAL NUMBER OF WORDS: 190

Comments:

Check the student's reading accuracy in the books recorded in the **Teacher Options** or read aloud in the classroom.

The Big Hill

(Readable 21)

"What a day!"

"Let's test our sleds today!" says Jed. "I have my big, red sled."

"I have my big, yellow sled," says Jessy.

They will test the sleds at the park. They go up a little hill.

Zip! Off they go on the sleds.

The sleds are fast! They can go so far. "That was the best," says Jessy.

Jed and Jessy see a big hill in the park. "We can test the sleds on that big hill," yells Jessy.

Up the big hill they go.

Zip! Down they go. The sleds are going fast, too fast!

The sleds are going far, too far! "Stop, stop!" yells Jed. "See the trees!"

Zip! They just miss the trees! They fall into the snow.

"That was not fun!" Jed tells Jessy. "Let's go back to the little hill."

"Yes," says Jessy, and off they go!

TOTAL NUMBER OF WORDS: 144

Comments:

Check the student's reading accuracy in the books recorded in the **Teacher Options** or read aloud in the classroom.

What's in the Egg?

(Readable 22)

Meg finds an egg in the barn. Is it a hen's egg or a duck's egg?

Meg goes to the vet. "Is this a hen's egg or a duck's egg?" asks Meg. The vet looks at the

egg.

"Put the egg in this hot box," says the vet. "Then you can find out what kind of egg it is."

Meg sets the box on the desk. She puts the egg in the hot box.

Days and days go by.

Then one day, ping! Meg sees the egg jump. Then crack! A bill pops out of the egg! Look! A

leg is coming out!

What is it?

"Quack, quack!" Meg has a pet duck! She rubs the duck's fuzz. Meg loves the duck!

TOTAL NUMBER OF WORDS: 122

Comments:

Check the student's reading accuracy in the books recorded in the **Teacher Options** or read aloud in the classroom.

Rom and His New Pet

(Readable 23)

Rom can go with his mother and father to the camp.

*He wants a pet. He will look for an elephant.

Rom is in his tent at the camp.

Thump, thump, thump! "What is it? What went thump, thump, thump?"

He sees a little elephant by a tree.

It is sad. It cannot bend its leg.

Rom goes to the elephant.

"You went thump, thump, thump!" says Rom. "You have a bump on your leg. Let me mend

it."

Rom mends the elephant's leg.

The elephant goes with Rom to the pond.

Rom scrubs the little elephant. The little elephant gets Rom wet!

Rom hugs his new pet. "You are my best friend!"

* The text on this line has been revised and may not match the text the student reads from. Please take this into account when scoring the student's reading accuracy.

TOTAL NUMBER OF WORDS: 113

Comments:

Check the student's reading accuracy in the books recorded in the **Teacher Options** or read aloud in the classroom.

Chet and Chuck

(Readable 24)

Chet Chimp is hanging from his branch.

He has an itch. He can scratch. He can twitch and scratch.

Can he clutch the branch and scratch?

Chuck Chipmunk is sitting by the tree.

His house shakes when Chet scratches.

"Stop that scratching! Stop that twitching! My house is shaking!" yells Chuck.

"I have some spots. They itch a lot!" says Chet.

"Oh my, you have the chicken pox!" says Chuck.

"Here is some pink stuff to put on your spots. It's the best thing if you itch a lot!"

"Oh thank you, thank you, thanks a lot! You are a friend! I feel so good!" says Chet.

"Me too," says Chuck.

TOTAL NUMBER OF WORDS: 111

Comments:

Check the student's reading accuracy in the books recorded in the **Teacher Options** or read aloud in the classroom.

What Do I Spy?

(Readable 25)

What do I spy?

I spy a fly.

It's all wet! It flips and flaps to get dry. Buzz, buzz!

I spy a sly fox.

She sits still down in the log. Why? A dog looks for her. Shh, shh!

I spy a pig in a plane.

The pig can try to fly the plane. He does tricks in the sky. Whiz, whiz!

I spy a crab in a shell.

She's too shy to come out. She slips into a crack in the rock. Click, click!

I spy a cat with a pan. He can fry a fish for lunch. How is it? Yum, yum!

How do I spy a fly, a fox, a pig, a crab, and a cat?

I spy them with my spy glass, and I spy them all from here!

TOTAL NUMBER OF WORDS: 133

Comments:

Check the student's reading accuracy in the books recorded in the **Teacher Options** or read aloud in the classroom.

Quick! Help!

(Review Readable 5)

1 man fell in a well. He is in a fix.

"I fell in the well!" yells the man. "Quick! Help!"

2 men come with nets. "We went for our nets. We can put them in the well!"

Can they get the man out? No! They can't!

3 men come with pets. "We led our pets to the well. Pets! Go fetch!" Can they get the man out? No! They can't!

A jet is in the sky. 4 men in vests jump out of the jet. "Land by the well! Let's go!" Can they get the man out? No! They can't!

5 men in a little red car stop by. "Get out! Get out! Come try!" Can they get the man out? No! They can't!

"Quick! Help!" yells the man in the well. Will they quit? No! Everyone at the well can help. Can they get the man out?

Yes! They can!

TOTAL NUMBER OF WORDS: 152

Comments:

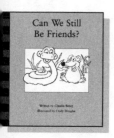

Check the student's reading accuracy in the books recorded in the **Teacher Options** or read aloud in the classroom.

Can We Still Be Friends?

(Readable 26)

Rex Rat is having a birthday party. Today he is six.

He wants to have cake and lemonade.

He will play tag. This is the game he likes best.

His friends Fred Frog and Pat Pig will come. But he is not sure his best friend, Sal Snake, will come.

Rex and Sal were in the mud this morning.

Rex had the rake.

Sal had the spade so she could plant pumpkins.

Rex said, "Let's trade so I can plant corn."

Sal said, "No, I want the spade!"

Sal went to her house mad.

Rex went to his house mad.

Tap, tap, tap. "Who is it?" said Rex.

"Let's be friends," said Sal. "Happy, happy birthday, Rex Rat!"

TOTAL NUMBER OF WORDS: 118

Comments:

Check the student's reading accuracy in the books recorded in the **Teacher Options** or read aloud in the classroom.

Fun in Kansas

(Readable 27)

Dane is going to see Grandma and Grandpa.

He will go on a plane.

He will go to their farm in Kansas.

They have many pigs and a big cow.

They have horses with black manes.

Dane loves to ride a horse down the lane to the big barn.

Grandpa has some hens. He lets Dane put the eggs in the crate.

Grandma makes cookies. She puts them on a plate for Grandpa and Dane.

Dane skates on the sidewalk by the house.

He can do a lot of fun things on the farm.

Dane will have so much fun in Kansas.

TOTAL NUMBER OF WORDS: 102

Comments:

Check the student's reading accuracy in the books recorded in the **Teacher Options** or read aloud in the classroom.

Brave Dave and Jane

(Readable 28)

Dave and Jane are on the plane.

They dare to walk on the plane's wing.

Dave is waving.

Jane is skating.

Dave is holding on to the wing.

Jane is holding on.

"Hold on! Hold on!"

"Pull the string!"

"Land in the square!"

"Look out for that tree!"

Crunch!

TOTAL NUMBER OF WORDS: 49

Comments:

Child's Name:_____

Check the student's reading accuracy in the books recorded in the **Teacher Options** or read aloud in the classroom.

My Snowman

(Readable 29)

My snowman stands by the house. He stands in the same place.

He is cold, but he is happy.

The snow is falling fast.

My snowman's face is cold. His black eyes can't shut.

He has red mitten hands.

His hat is made from a page of the newspaper.

Earmuffs are on his ears.

Oh look! The sun is out! My snowman is getting hot.

He is melting.

All that is left is my snowman's smile.

TOTAL NUMBER OF WORDS: 76

Comments:

Check the student's reading accuracy in the books recorded in the **Teacher Options** or read aloud in the classroom.

Space Chase Race

(Review Readable 6)

Hurry! Hurry! Do not be late to the big chase!

Space monsters fly planes in the race. They race to chase the space snake into his square

cage. They want to win the Crazy Case.

Wade is upset.

His space plane will not go fast.

The blade on the plane wobbles.

He has to brace the blade so he can fly fast.

Can he get to the blade if he stands on a crate?

He wishes he had a spare blade. But he will have to save this blade.

Maybe he can put duct tape on the blade to fix it!

"Hurry! Hurry! Go, blade, go!" Hiss! Click! Zip! "Come on, plane!"

Varoom! Off goes Wade. Wade's plane is fast.

Hooray! Wade wins the Crazy Case.

TOTAL NUMBER OF WORDS: 126

Comments:

Check the student's reading accuracy in the books recorded in the **Teacher Options** or read aloud in the classroom.

Oh No, Mose!

(Readable 30)

"Grab the scope! Grab the scope! Mose just fell down the slope!"

"Mose fell down the slope? Oh no! Can you see him with the scope?"

"Where is he? Where is Mose?"

"I can see him by that rose. He fell down and hit his nose."

"Can we get him up the slope?" "With a rope we can, I hope."

"What? No rope? Then grab the hose! Would you toss it down to Mose?"

"Oh no! A bee is on the rose."

"Oh, Mose, look out! It's by your nose!"

"Toss the hose! Toss the scope!"

"Here comes Mose up the slope!"

"Come in the house. Run in here, Mose!"

"The bee is out. We saved your nose!"

TOTAL NUMBER OF WORDS: 118

Comments:

Check the student's reading accuracy in the books recorded in the **Teacher Options** or read aloud in the classroom.

Smoke!

(Readable 31)

"What is that?" said Cole the mole.

"What is that smell?"

"Oh no, I smell smoke!" said the small mole.

From his room in the hole, Cole slid down the pole to wake up the mole family.

He woke up his mother. "This isn't a joke." said Cole. "I smell smoke!"

He woke up his father. "This isn't a joke. I smell smoke! Hurry, we do not want to choke from

the smoke!" said Cole.

Mother, Father, and Cole, the small mole, came up from their home down in the hole.

"Up the slope!" said Mother.

"Over the hill!" said Cole.

"Oh no!" said Father. "Look! It's the smoke from their grill!"

So it was just a joke, just a little bit of smoke," said Cole.

Let's eat!

TOTAL NUMBER OF WORDS: 128

Comments:

Check the student's reading accuracy in the books recorded in the **Teacher Options** or read aloud in the classroom.

The Note
(Readable 32)

Max and Sam see a stone. On the stone is a note.

"Look! A note is on the stone," says Max. "What does it say?" he asks Sam.

"The note is in code," says Sam. "I can't read it."

"Mr. Bones can read code!" says Max. "Let's get him to read the note."

Max and Sam take the bus to the home of Mr. Bones.

"Please, Mr. Bones, will you look at this note?" asks Sam. "The note is in code," says Max.

"Can you read the code, Mr. Bones?"

"I can read any code, yes, I can," says Mr. Bones. "Slone, bring me my magnifying glass."

Slone runs to get the magnifying glass for Mr. Bones.

"Here is the magnifying glass," says Slone. "Good, now I can read the code on the note,"

says Mr. Bones.

"The note reads, 'Come home for an ice cream cone. Love, Mother,'" says Mr. Bones.

"Hurry! Let's go!" says Max.

"We are glad you can read the code, Mr. Bones," say Max and Sam.

TOTAL NUMBER OF WORDS: 190

Comments:

Check the student's reading accuracy in the books recorded in the **Teacher Options** or read aloud in the classroom.

The Snoring Boar

(Readable 33)

It is a chore to live next door to a boar that snores.

I hid by the stove, tore my robe when I dove, all because of the snores of that boar from next door.

I went to the store to get something more for my ears that are sore from the snores of that boar.

In my red truck I drove to the shore of the cove, so I would not hear more of the snores of that boar.

I sat by the shore, and I said with a roar, "I can't stand any more of the snores from that boar!"

I went back to my home, called him up on the phone and said, "Please, Mr. Boar, do not snore anymore."

"Sure," said the boar, "I will not snore anymore."

It's not a chore to live next door to a boar who doesn't snore anymore.

TOTAL NUMBER OF WORDS: 150

Comments:

Check the student's reading accuracy in the books recorded in the **Teacher Options** or read aloud in the classroom.

Shopping Day

(Review Readable 7)

Where can we go today?

Let's go shopping!

Dad wants to get a new fishing pole.

Mom wants to look at roses.

Tim and Jill want to go to the pet store. "Just to look," says Mom.

At the pet store, Tim and Jill see a dog with a bone. They want a dog.

"No dog," says Dad. "No dog," says Mom.

Dad looks at fishing poles. He hopes to pick a good pole.

Tim and Jill vote that Dad gets the red pole, but he picks the black pole.

At the flower store, the roses smell so good! Tim's and Jill's noses have fun. Look out! Those

roses can poke you.

They stop to get snow cones for a snack.

"Let's go home," says Mom. "But where is Dad?" asks Tim.

What a fun day!

TOTAL NUMBER OF WORDS: 136

Comments:

Check the student's reading accuracy in the books recorded in the **Teacher Options** or read aloud in the classroom.

Friends

(Readable 34)

Jess and Jenny play in the park.

They like to slide. They glide down fast.

Sometimes they slide at the same time.

They can sit side by side in the wide swing. Up, up and down, down.

They like to run and hide.

"Jenny, run and hide," says Jess. "1, 2, 3, 4, 5, 6, 7, 8, 9, 10. I will find you if you hide."

"Look, I see you!" "Now it's time for you to look for me," says Jess.

The sun is hot. They want something cold.

Jess can buy an ice cream cone for a dime.

Jenny can buy a limeade.

"What a fun day!" says Jess.

Jenny says, "Let's come back tomorrow."

TOTAL NUMBER OF WORDS: 116

Comments:

Check the student's reading accuracy in the books recorded in the **Teacher Options** or read aloud in the classroom.

Two Little Pines

(Readable 35)

Two little pines stand side by side. They stand in a line by the school.

The sun shines. One little pine starts to whine.

"Why are you sad?" asks Pam Pine.

"I don't want the sun to shine," whines Pete Pine. "The wind will start. Then the nine kids in that room will fly kites."

"I am quite sure that a kite will get stuck in my branches! I will have a red or white kite stuck here all summer," says Pete.

"That is quite fine. All you have to do is wiggle, and it will come down," says Pam.

"Wiggle?" asks Pete. "Yes, wiggle!" says Pam. "Like this."

"Ooo, that feels good! Bring on those kites!" says Pete.

TOTAL NUMBER OF WORDS: 119

Comments:

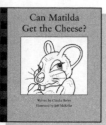

Check the student's reading accuracy in the books recorded in the **Teacher Options** or read aloud in the classroom.

Can Matilda Get the Cheese?

(Readable 36)

"Oh, look at that nice pile of cheese!" yells Matilda.

"It is just what mice like to eat. I want one or two slices of cheese now!"

Matilda looks at the pile on the plate.

She looks at the cat under the table. Matilda will never get that cheese.

Then she looks at the tire swing. A wire holds it to the tree.

Matilda likes to swing from that tire.

Matilda smiles.

She looks at the tire. She looks at the cheese.

She gets in the swing and swings up and down, up and down.

Get that cheese!

"Yippee!"

TOTAL NUMBER OF WORDS: 99

Comments:

Check the student's reading accuracy in the books recorded in the **Teacher Options** or read aloud in the classroom.

Let's Go to Yellowstone

(Readable 37)

We are going on a trip to Yellowstone.

We will drive there in the car. We will stay for five days. What a happy bunch! Can we go now?

Will there be bears? We would like to see a mother bear and her cubs.

We want to hike to see the geysers. They go up fast, and they are so hot!

Riding our bikes to see new places will be fun. We hope we do not see a skunk with stripes!

It will be fun to fish in the lake because Grandpa knows how to fish.

We will eat the fish for lunch.

We are going to have so much fun! Let's go now!

TOTAL NUMBER OF WORDS: 114

Comments:

Check the student's reading accuracy in the books recorded in the **Teacher Options** or read aloud in the classroom.

Maddy and Clive

(Review Readable 8)

Maddy loves summer. There are so many things she likes to do.

She likes to hike. She hikes in the hills by her house. She takes her dog, Clive, with her.

Clive runs and jumps and hikes with Maddy. Sometimes Maddy hikes five miles, but Clive never gripes or whines.

Maddy likes to ride her bike with the white stripes. She likes to ride to the top of the hill and then glide down. Clive rides fast, too.

Sometimes Maddy and Clive like to swim. It is so nice when the sun is hot.

They slide down a rope swing and make a big splash.

The best time of all is the end of the day. Maddy and Clive sit under the tree and eat watermelon.

Maddy and Clive have big smiles!

TOTAL NUMBER OF WORDS: 132

Comments:

Check the student's reading accuracy in the books recorded in the **Teacher Options** or read aloud in the classroom.

Brute and the Flute

(Readable 38)

Libby went to the store. She got a new flute.

She can play the flute and skip around her room. Around and around the room she skips.

She pokes her dog, Brute.

"Look at me, Brute. Look at me skip and play the flute. Don't I look cute?"

Brute does not think Libby is cute. Brute thinks she is rude.

Brute wants to take his nap.

Brute jumps up and bites the flute.

He runs out of the room. "Stop, Brute, stop!" yells Libby.

Brute runs fast!

He runs to his doghouse and hides the flute.

Now Brute can take his nap!

TOTAL NUMBER OF WORDS: 102

Comments:

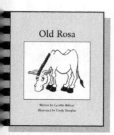

Check the student's reading accuracy in the books recorded in the **Teacher Options** or read aloud in the classroom.

Old Rosa

(Readable 39)

Old Rosa is a mule. She's very old, but she can do a lot of work.

She can pull the wagon for Father.

Mother takes Old Rosa into town to shop. She can bring things home on Old Rosa's back.

Sometimes Old Rosa goes with Luis up the hill to see his friend Anita. Old Rosa lets Luis ride

on her back.

Anita thinks Old Rosa is cute. She likes to brush Old Rosa's mane.

Old Rosa likes sugar cubes. Anita has some for her to eat.

At the end of the day, Rosa gets to rest.

Everyone loves Old Rosa. She is the best mule around.

TOTAL NUMBER OF WORDS: 107

Comments:

Check the student's reading accuracy in the books recorded in the **Teacher Options** or read aloud in the classroom.

What Is in the Tree?

(Readable 40)

Every day June fixes trees. Today she'll fix the big shade tree next to the white house.

She goes way up into the tree.

She must prune every branch. She will use a saw to prune the tree.

Zzzip, zzzip, zzzip. She cuts the branches down.

June stops. What does she hear?

*Is someone humming a tune? Could someone be crying?

Look, there in the tree! It's Fluffy the cat.

*She can't find her way down. She's stuck in the tree.

June gets Fluffy and takes her down to the house.

Fluffy rubs June's leg and purrs. She is so happy!

June is happy, too. Now she can get back to work!

* The text on this line has been revised and may not match the text the student reads from. Please take this into account when scoring the student's reading accuracy.

TOTAL NUMBER OF WORDS: 123

Comments:

Check the student's reading accuracy in the books recorded in the **Teacher Options** or read aloud in the classroom.

Too Much Popcorn

(Readable 41)

Ming and Greg loved to skate! They skated every day. They skated by the house.

They skated over to the school. They skated around the trees.

Then it began to rain. It rained and rained and rained! "We'd better go inside," said Ming.

"What can we do now?" asked Greg. "Let's play games," said Ming.

They played cards. They played chess.

They played hide and seek.

"I want something to eat," said Greg. "What can we find to snack on?" said Ming.

"Let's make popcorn," said Greg. "We can make a lot of popcorn!"

The popcorn popped and popped and popped...

And popped!

"Look, look!" yelled Ming. "What will we do with all this popcorn?"

"There's just one thing to do," said Greg. "EAT IT!"

TOTAL NUMBER OF WORDS: 125

Comments:

Check the student's reading accuracy in the books recorded in the **Teacher Options** or read aloud in the classroom.

Old King Dune

(Review Readable 9)

Old King Dune ruled the land of Cube. He was a very good king.

He wanted to help everyone in Cube so they could all be happy.

Every morning he fed the people milk and pancakes.

Then they went to work.

Everyone had jobs in the land of Cube, and they all helped one another.

*The people in Cube used no money. They gave each other cute presents.

At the end of the day, the people gathered in the square.

The king's cute wife, June, played tunes on her flute while the people skipped and hopped

around the square.

Then King Dune began to tell silly stories.

*They were so funny that when the king finished, the people yelled for more.

*"Tomorrow," said the king, "I will tell you more stories."

*The people in the land of Cube were all very happy, thanks to King Dune!

* The text on this line has been revised and may not match the text the student reads from. Please take this into account when scoring the student's reading accuracy.

TOTAL NUMBER OF WORDS: 169

Comments:

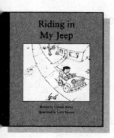

Check the student's reading accuracy in the books recorded in the **Teacher Options** or read aloud in the classroom.

Riding in My Jeep

(Readable 42)

Riding, riding up and down my street.

My little jeep goes when I push my feet.

It has two pedals that I push up and down.

I go where I want in my hometown.

The jeep is green. The hubcaps are chrome.

I ride down the hill in back of my home.

When I get to the top and I want to speed,

I feel like I'm flying. My feet I don't need!

I bump over rocks and on down the lane.

Bumping and thumping, I'm so glad I came.

If you come to my street on some sunny day,

You can ride in my jeep. I'll show you the way.

TOTAL NUMBER OF WORDS: 112

Comments:

Check the student's reading accuracy in the books recorded in the **Teacher Options** or read aloud in the classroom.

Sammy and Pete

(Readable 43)

Sammy is a brand-new seal.

He is so weak that he can't speak. He can only squeak to let his mother know what he needs.

All he seems to do is sleep, dream, and eat. Pete Penguin knows that Sammy was born today. He can't wait to meet Sammy.

Pete is little, too. He hopes that he and Sammy will be friends.

Pete pokes his beak around the rock. He wants to sneak a peek at the new baby seal.

"When can Sammy come play in the stream?" Pete asks Sammy's mother.

"Tomorrow Sammy can meet you, Pete. Tomorrow you can teach him to play in the stream and slide on the ice. Then you can help him meet all your other friends."

"Hooray!" says Pete. "Sh-sh-sh!" says Sammy's mother. "Sammy is sleeping."

TOTAL NUMBER OF WORDS: 133

Comments:

Check the student's reading accuracy in the books recorded in the **Teacher Options** or read aloud in the classroom.

Will You Play with Me?

(Readable 44)

One spring day a little snail hatched.

"Here I am, World!" it yelled, but there wasn't anyone around to hear. "I'm all alone," thought the snail. "I need to find someone to play with."

The little snail saw a trail. "This looks like a good place to start," thought the snail, and it slipped down the trail.

While on the trail, a quail crossed the snail's path. "Will you play with me?" asked the little snail.

"Goodness, no! I need to find some hay so I can lay my eggs!" huffed the quail, as she bobbed the other way.

"Oh well!" thought the snail, and it slithered down the trail again.

Soon, a little gray puppy crossed the snail's path. "Will you play with me?" asked the snail.

"No way! I snagged my tail on a nail, and I'm in too much pain!" wailed the puppy, as it ran on its way.

"Oh well!" thought the snail, and it slimed down the trail again.

The trail ended at a little stream. The snail slid onto a leaf to sail across.

*When the snail got to the other side, rain began to fall. "Oh no!" yelled the snail, as it hid under the leaf.

After a while, the little snail peeked to see if it was safe to come out. It saw three other snails.

"Why are you under a leaf?" one asked. "Snails LOVE to play in the rain!" yelled another.

"Come out and play with us, silly snail!" smiled the last.

And the little snail did.

* The text on this line has been revised and may not match the text the student reads from. Please take this into account when scoring the student's reading accuracy.

TOTAL NUMBER OF WORDS: 171

Comments:

Check the student's reading accuracy in the books recorded in the **Teacher Options** or read aloud in the classroom.

The Rescue

(Readable 45)

One day two best friends, Goat and Toad, went for a walk.

They saw an old bridge. The bridge went across a moat.

Toad hopped onto the bridge, and it began to shake!

"Run, Toad! It will fall!" Goat yelled. Toad ran as the bridge moaned.

Just as Toad jumped off, the old bridge broke with a crash.

Toad was stuck.

Goat did not know what to do. He sat on the grass and thought.

Goat saw a boat, but he didn't see the hole in it!

He got in and began to float. The boat went down, down, down.

Toad saw Goat in the moat. "I'll help you, Goat!" Toad yelled.

Toad jumped in the moat to save his friend.

He swam to a floating oar and gave it to Goat.

They both swam to dry land.

Then Toad began to laugh. He laughed and laughed and laughed.

Goat said, "Why are you laughing?"

"Toads can float! I can float! Why didn't I just swim across the moat?"

TOTAL NUMBER OF WORDS: 169

Comments:

Check the student's reading accuracy in the books recorded in the **Teacher Options** or read aloud in the classroom.

Who Am I?

(Review Readable 10)

My home is in the rain forest in South America.

I am green, red, and gray with a yellow throat. You may say that I am very handsome.

I have no hair, and I never need a coat.

Three toes are on each of my two feet.

I have a big beak, but no teeth, so I don't have to brush.

I eat seeds and grains. Nuts are real treat. But I never eat meat!

I can tweet, squeak, scream, laugh, or sing. Sometimes I can even speak like you.

My ears are hidden, but I can hear very well.

I have two big wings, and I can fly. I can fly way up in the sky and dive down.

When it is dark outside, I'm not afraid because I can hide in my big, safe tree and go to

sleep.

Who am I?

I am Paco Pancho Parrot, mi amigo!

TOTAL NUMBER OF WORDS: 152

Comments:

• Unit 10 / Review Lesson

SECTION K

CHECK SHEETS

WRITING RUBRICS

Name:_____

Editing Rubric

Criteria	Always (4)	Usually (3)	Sometimes (2)	Never (1)	Comments
Sentences					
Writes in complete sentences					
Capitals					
Capitalizes the first word in a sentence					
Capitalizes proper nouns					
End Punctuation					
Uses periods appropriately					
Uses question marks appropriately					
Uses exclamation marks appropriately					
Apostrophe					
Uses apostrophes to show possessives					
Uses apostrophes correctly in contractions					
Quotations					
Places quotation marks correctly					

Name:_____

Revision Rubric

Criteria	Always (4)	Usually (3)	Sometimes (2)	Never (1)	Comments
Character, Plot, and Setting					
Uses characters in prewriting, rough, and final drafts					
Uses setting in prewriting, rough, and final drafts					
Has a beginning, middle, and end					

Name:_____

Revision Rubric

Criteria	Always (4)	Usually (3)	Sometimes (2)	Never (1)	Comments
Character, Plot, and Setting					
Uses characters in prewriting, rough, and final drafts					
Uses setting in prewriting, rough, and final drafts					
Has a beginning, middle, and end					

Student's Writing Checklist

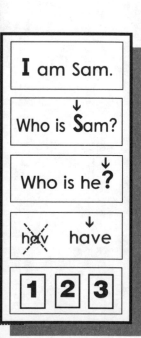

Criteria	YES	NO
Did I start each sentence with a **capital letter**?		
Did I capitalize **proper nouns**?		
Did I use the right **sentence end marks**?		
Did I check my **spelling**?		
Does my story have a **beginning, middle,** and **end**?		

Name:_____

Student's Writing Checklist

Criteria	YES	NO
Did I start each sentence with a **capital letter**?		
Did I capitalize **proper nouns**?		
Did I use the right **sentence end marks**?		
Did I check my **spelling**?		
Does my story have a **beginning, middle,** and **end**?		

SECTION L

CHECK SHEETS

DICTATION SHEETS

Capital Letters

1. _____
2. _____
3. _____
4. _____

5. _____
6. _____
7. _____
8. _____

9. _____
10. _____
11. _____
12. _____

13. _____
14. _____
15. _____
16. _____

17. _____
18. _____
19. _____
20. _____

21. _____
22. _____
23. _____
24. _____

25. _____
26. _____

Lowercase Letters

1. _____
2. _____
3. _____
4. _____

5. _____
6. _____
7. _____
8. _____

9. _____
10. _____
11. _____
12. _____

13. _____
14. _____
15. _____
16. _____

17. _____
18. _____
19. _____
20. _____

21. _____
22. _____
23. _____
24. _____

25. _____
26. _____

Letter Sounds

1. _____
   - - - - - - - - - - -
   _____

2. _____
   - - - - - - - - - - -
   _____

3. _____
   - - - - - - - - - - -
   _____

4. _____
   - - - - - - - - - - -
   _____

5. _____
   - - - - - - - - - - -
   _____

6. _____
   - - - - - - - - - - -
   _____

7. _____
   - - - - - - - - - - -
   _____

8. _____
   - - - - - - - - - - -
   _____

9. _____
   - - - - - - - - - - -
   _____

10. _____
    - - - - - - - - - - -
    _____

11. _____
    - - - - - - - - - - -
    _____

12. _____
    - - - - - - - - - - -
    _____

13. _____
    - - - - - - - - - - -
    _____

14. _____
    - - - - - - - - - - -
    _____

15. _____
    - - - - - - - - - - -
    _____

16. _____
    - - - - - - - - - - -
    _____

17. _____
    - - - - - - - - - - -
    _____

18. _____
    - - - - - - - - - - -
    _____

19. _____
    - - - - - - - - - - -
    _____

20. _____
    - - - - - - - - - - -
    _____

21. _____
    - - - - - - - - - - -
    _____

22. _____
    - - - - - - - - - - -
    _____

23. _____
    - - - - - - - - - - -
    _____

24. _____
    - - - - - - - - - - -
    _____

25. _____
    - - - - - - - - - - -
    _____

26. _____
    - - - - - - - - - - -
    _____

CVC Words

1. _____

2. _____

3. _____

4. _____

5. _____

6. _____

7. _____

8. _____

9. _____

10. _____

11. _____

12. _____

13. _____

14. _____

15. _____

16. _____

17. _____

18. _____

19. _____

20. _____

21. _____

22. _____

23. _____

24. _____

25. _____

26. _____

SECTION M

WORKSHEETS

LETTER WORKSHEETS

Name

Dictation: Slant down, slant down, across — capital *A*

Dictation: Over, curve around, up, down — lowercase *a*

Dictation: Down, curve around, curve around — capital *B*

B B B B B B

B B B B B B

r r r r r r

Dictation: Down, up, curve around — lowercase *b*

b b b b b b

b b b b b b

Dictation: Up, over, curve around, up — capital C

C C C C C C

Dictation: Up, over, curve around, up — lowercase c

c c c c c c

Name

Dictation: Down, curve around — capital *D*

D D D D D D

Dictation: Over, curve around, up high, down — lowercase *d*

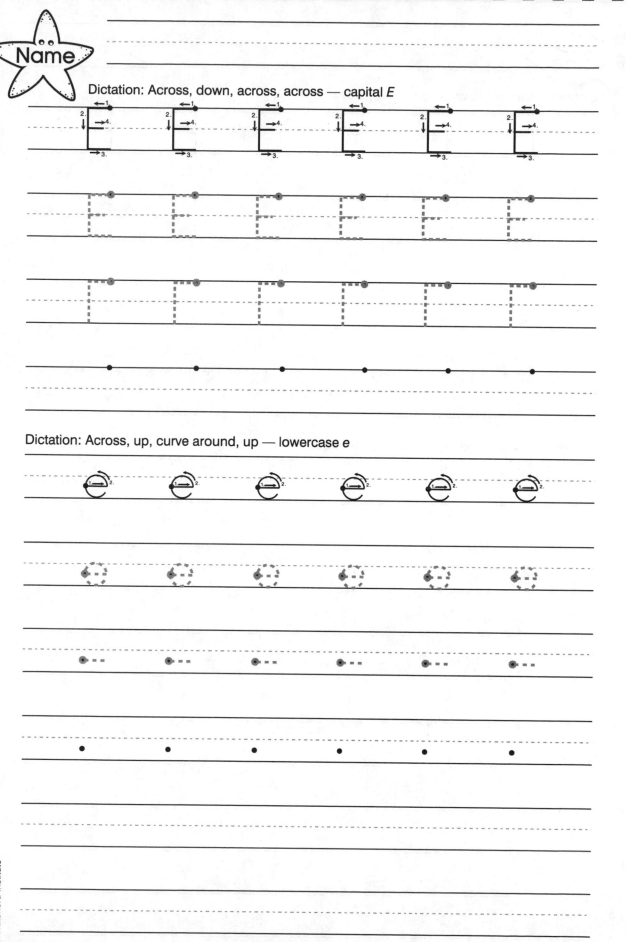

Name

Dictation: Across, down, across, across — capital *E*

Dictation: Across, up, curve around, up — lowercase *e*

Name

Dictation: Across, down, across — capital *F*

Dictation: Up, over, down, lift, cross — lowercase *f*

Dictation: Curve around, in — capital G

Dictation: Over, curve around, up, down below, curve up — lowercase g

Dictation: Down, down, across — capital *H*

Dictation: Down, up, curve over, down — lowercase *h*

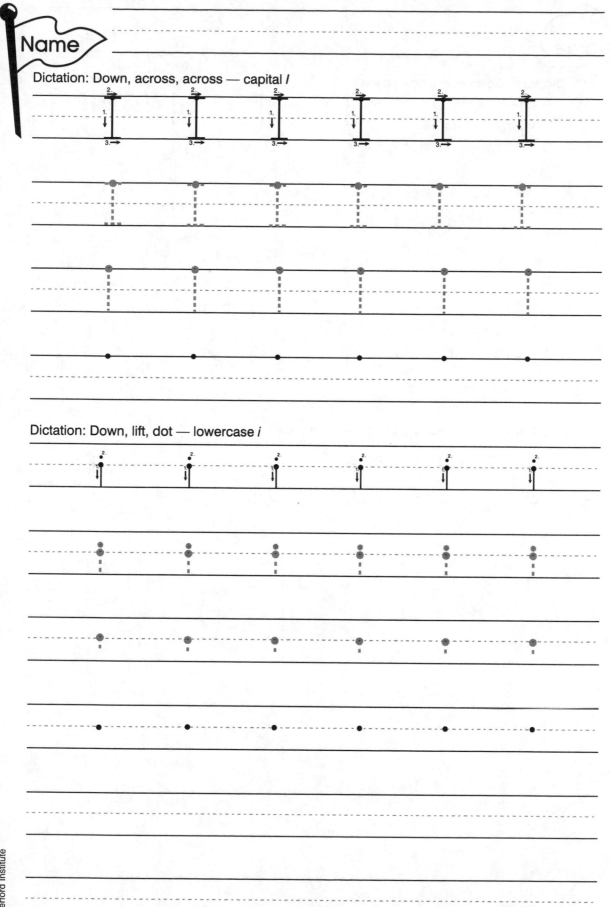

Name

Dictation: Down, across, across — capital I

Dictation: Down, lift, dot — lowercase i

Name

Dictation: Down, curve up — capital *J*

J J J J J J

Dictation: Down below, curve up, lift, dot — lowercase *j*

j j j j j j

Name

Dictation: Down, slant in, slant out — capital *K*

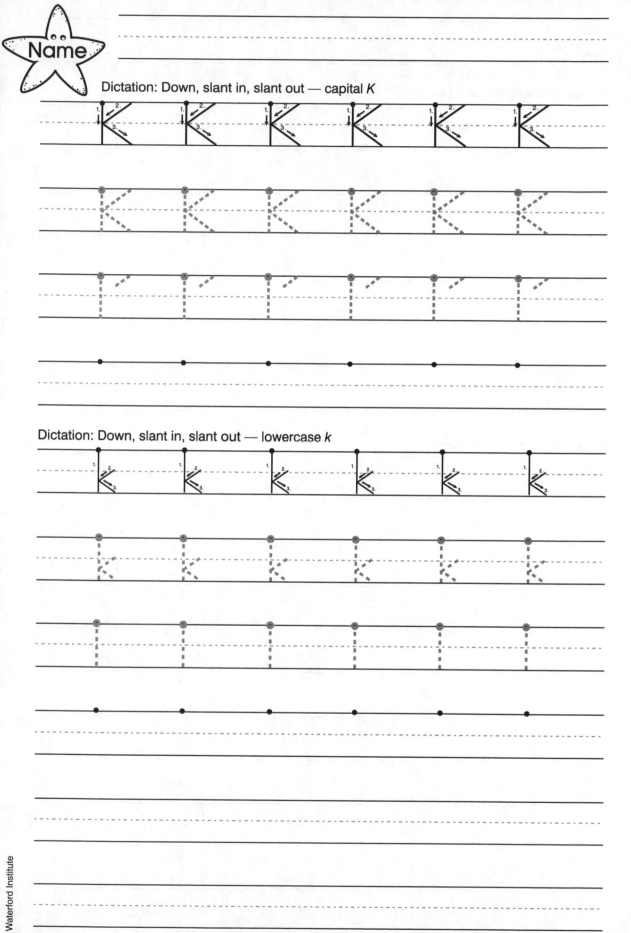

Dictation: Down, slant in, slant out — lowercase *k*

Name

Dictation: Down, across — capital *L*

Dictation: Down — lowercase *l*

Name

Dictation: Down, slant down, slant up, down — capital *M*

Dictation: Down, up, curve over, down, up, curve over, down — lowercase *m*

Dictation: Down, slant down, up — capital *N*

Dictation: Down, up, curve over, down — lowercase *n*

Dictation: Over, curve around, close — capital *O*

Dictation: Over, curve around, close — lowercase *o*

Name

Dictation: Down, curve around — capital *P*

P P P P P P

P P P P P P

Dictation: Down below, up, curve around — lowercase *p*

p p p p p p

p p p p p p

Name

Dictation: Curve around, slant down — capital Q

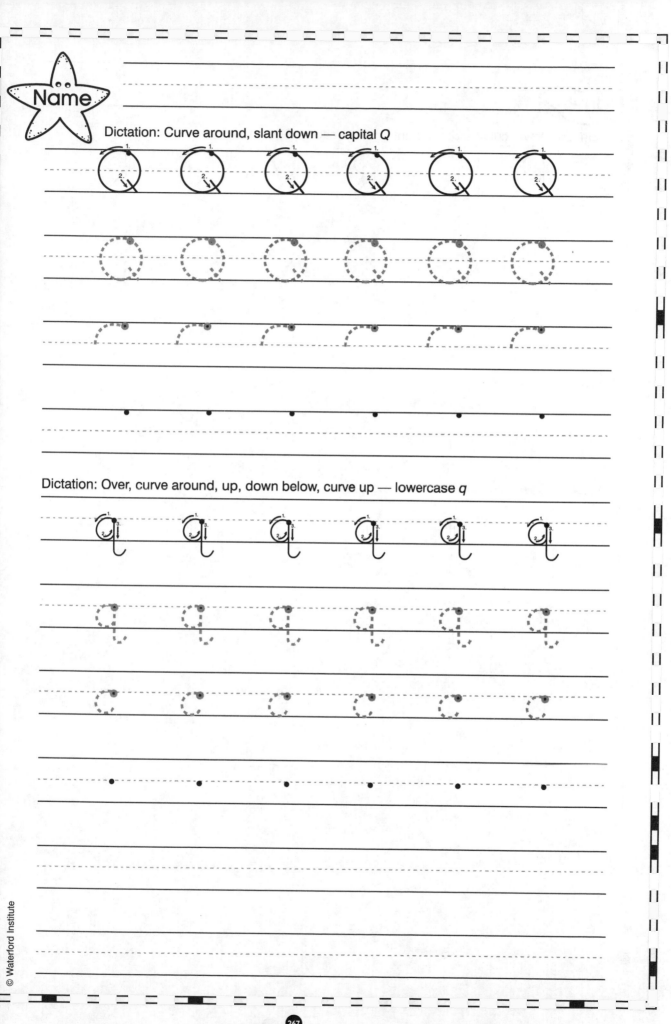

Dictation: Over, curve around, up, down below, curve up — lowercase q

Dictation: Down, curve around, slant down — capital *R*

Dictation: Down, up, curve over — lowercase *r*

Dictation: Up, over, curve around, curve around, up — capital *S*

Dictation: Up, over, curve around, curve around, up — lowercase *s*

Dictation: Down, across — capital *T*

Dictation: Down, lift, cross — lowercase *t*

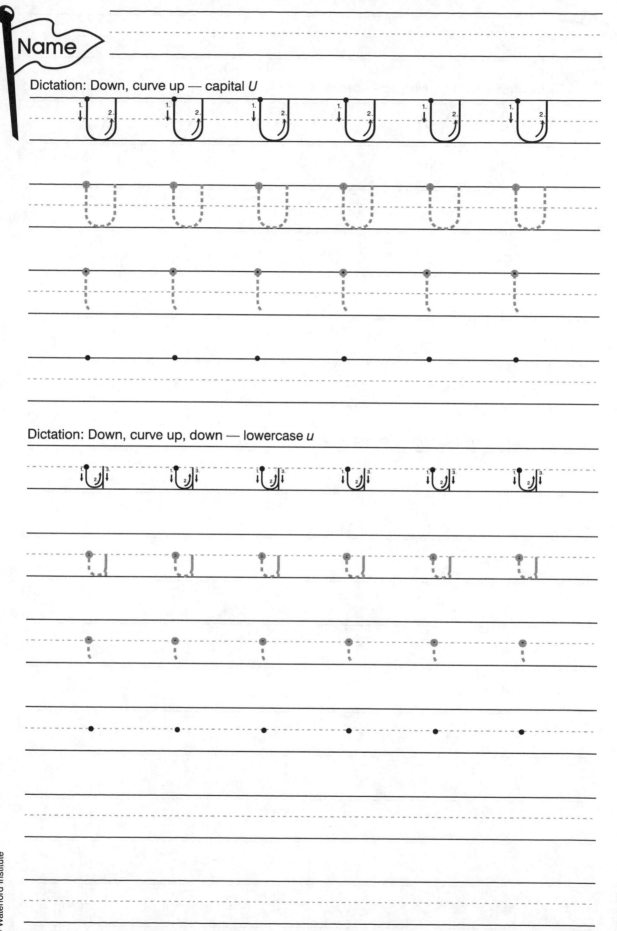

Name

Dictation: Down, curve up — capital U

Dictation: Down, curve up, down — lowercase u

© Waterford Institute

271

Dictation: Slant down, slant up — capital V

Dictation: Slant down, slant up — lowercase v

Dictation: Slant down, slant up, slant down, slant up — capital W

W W W W W W

W W W W W W

V V V V V V

Dictation: Slant down, slant up, slant down, slant up — lowercase w

W W W W W W

W W W W W W

V V V V V V

Dictation: Slant down, slant down — capital X

Dictation: Slant down, slant down — lowercase x

Name

Dictation: Slant down, slant down, down — capital *Y*

Dictation: Slant down, slant down, below — lowercase *y*

Dictation: Across, slant down, across — capital Z

Dictation: Across, slant down, across — lowercase z

SECTION N

WORKSHEETS

ON MY OWN WORKSHEETS

• Circle the letter that has the same beginning sound as the picture.

m f   p l   z r

• Write the word on the line.

me   me _____

is   _____

it   _____

on   _____

a   _____

• Me (A)

Name _____

• Write the letter that has the same beginning sound as the picture.

----- s -----

• Write the word on the line.

what

the   -------------------

in   -------------------

• Write the letter that has the same beginning sound as the picture.

m

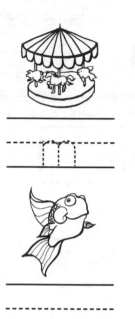

• Write the missing letters to complete the alphabet.

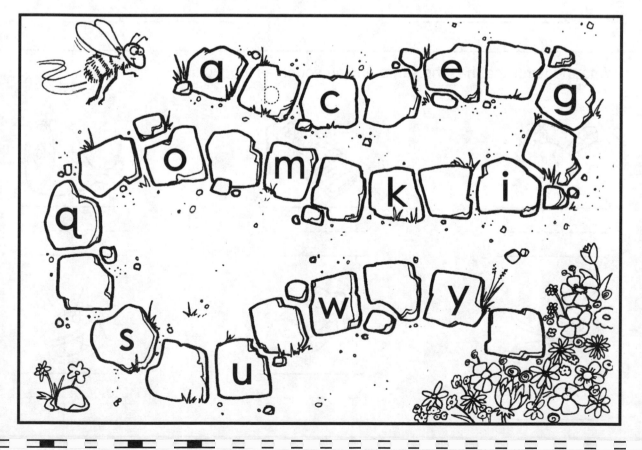

• I Am Sam (1A) / What Am I? (1B)

• Write each word from the list below the matching pattern.

Dad ~~Dad~~   **am**   **mad**   **sad**   **Sam**

ad

Dad

am

_____

• Write the letter that has the same ending sound as the picture.

d

• Write the missing letter to complete the ABC pattern.

a b c   BUS

f g   BUS

k l   BUS

• Write each name plus an 's to see who owns the hats.

Matt   + 's = Matt's   hat

Tad   + 's = _____ hat

Sam   + 's = _____ hat

Dad   + 's = _____ hat

• Add an *s* to the word to make it mean more than one. Then complete the sentences.

cat   +   s   =
cats

ant   +   s   =
_____

1. The _____ ran.

2. The _____ ran.

• Fill in the blank with the word from the Word Box that fits the pattern.

hat   mat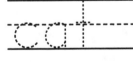
cat
_____

sad   Dad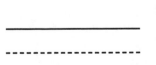
_____

band   hand   _____

Word Box

sand

~~cat~~

mad

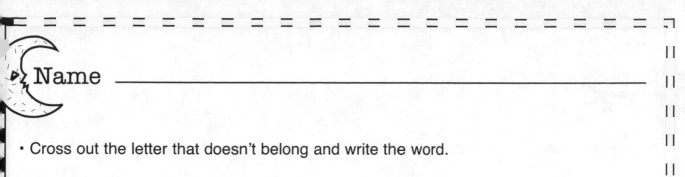
Name _____

• Cross out the letter that doesn't belong and write the word.

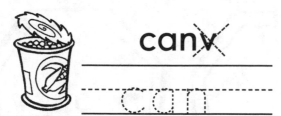 can~~x~~

can

stampf

_____

catx

_____

kmap

_____

_____

• A sentence tells a complete idea. Circle the sentence.

Pat

(Pat is at the camp.)

is sad

Ann is sad.

I can have a nap.

can have

• Write the missing letter to complete the ABC pattern.

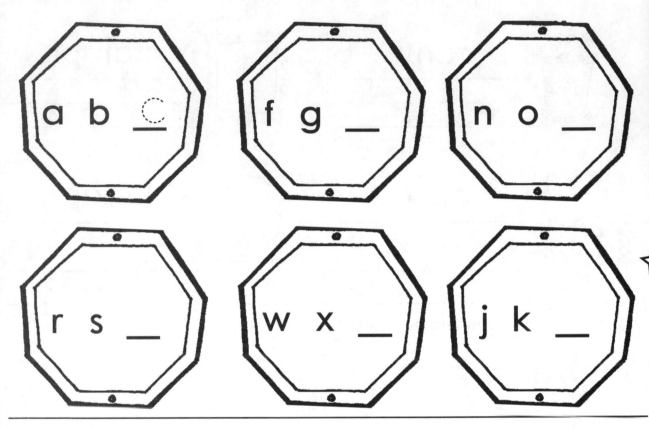

a b _c_

f g _

n o _

r s _

w x _

j k _

• Write each word from the list below the matching pattern.

stop map ~~nap~~ top cap mop

ap	op
nap	

• Write the letter or letters that have the same beginning sound as the picture.

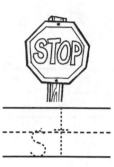

s t

- - - - - - -

- - - - - - -

- - - - - - -

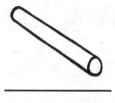

- - - - - - -

- - - - - - -

• Write the words in the order that makes a sentence.

1.   crab. Bob has a

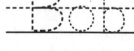 Bob

2.   sees a crab. Tab

- - - - - - -

 Name _____

• A sentence begins with a capital letter and ends with a period.
  Write these sentences correctly.

1. you have a box

You

2. rox can go fast

_____

_____

• Add an *es* to the word to make it mean more than one. Then complete the sentences.

box   +   es   =   boxes

fox   +   es   =   _____

1. He has the _____ .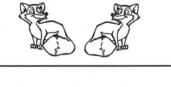

2. The _____ ran.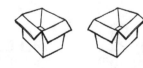

• Write the word. Then draw a line to the picture in the box that rhymes with the word.

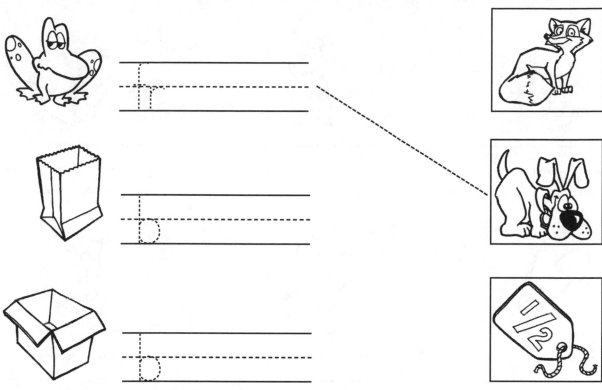

_____

• Color the words that end with *-og* and *-ob* green.
  Color the words that end with *-ag* and *-ab* yellow.

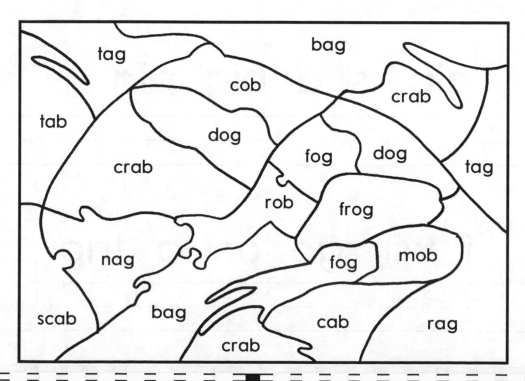

tag   bag
cob   crab
tab   dog
crab   fog   dog   tag
rob   frog
nag   fog   mob
scab   bag   cab   rag
crab

• A noun is a word that names people, places, or things. Write a noun below each picture.

crab

_____

_____

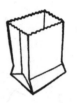

_____

_____

_____

• Write the sentences correctly.

1. pip is a big pig

Pip

2. i will go on a trip

_____

• Look at each pattern in the box. Add letters to the pattern to make new words.

p̶ s f	d p̶ b	p̶ b f
it	ig	in
pit	pig	pin

• A sentence that asks a question ends with a question mark.
A sentence that tells something ends with a period.
Put the correct punctuation mark at the end of each sentence.

1. What is in the pit ?

2. Tim has a nap ☐

3. Here is my hat ☐

4. What is in my hat ☐

• Write the missing letter to complete the ABC pattern.

• An exclamation mark shows excitement. Write each word with an exclamation mark. Then read the word with feeling.

stop   stop!

scat   _____

snap   _____

pop   _____

hiss   _____

go   _____

• Put the correct punctuation mark at the end of each sentence.

1. Who is bringing the milk ☐

2. Is she napping ☐

3. Let's eat ☐

4. Can I see the cat ☐

5. Todd can pat the cat ☐

• Write the ending pattern for each picture. You will need to write more than one letter.

ing

_____

_____

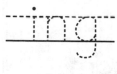

_in_

_____

_____

• Write the word from the Word Box that matches the picture.
  Add an *s* if there is more than one.

_____

- - - - - - - - - - - - - - - - - - - -

_____

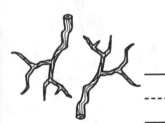

_____

- - - - - - - - - - - - - - - - - - - -

_____

_____

- - - - - - - - - - - - - - - - - - - -

_____

Word Box

sock
stick
pack

• Find all the words in the Word Box that are hidden in the big square. Circle the words as
  you find them. They can be read across ⟶ or down ↓.

w	t	e	x	n	b	e
i	o	k	s	b	d	c
y	o	u	r	k	o	l
h	a	j	r	e	c	a
r	f	r	o	m	o	z
g	v	u	g	v	m	h
o	b	i	d	h	e	r

Word Box

~~be~~

your

from

her

come

too

• Write the sentences correctly.

1.   are the fish in the pond

Are

2.   a dog can splash

• Color the words that end with *-ack, -ock, and -ick* blue.
  Color the words that end with *-ash* and *-ish* red.

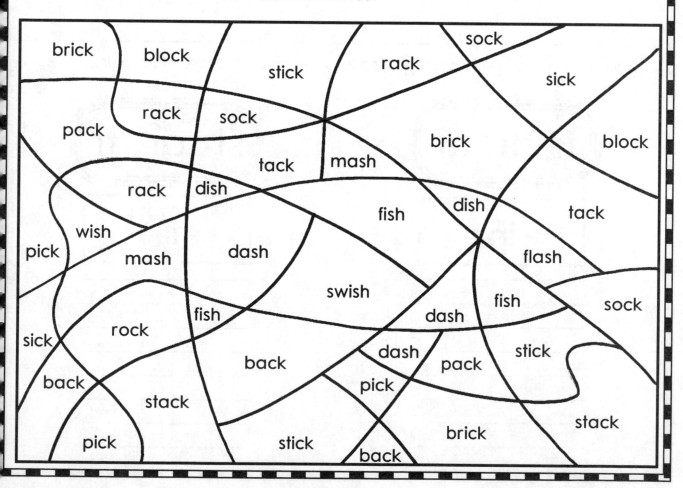

• A noun is a word that names people, places, or things. Look at the words under the pictures. Circle the noun.

person	place	thing

glad (man)   hill big   bug fun

• Look at the pattern in the box. Add blends to the pattern to make new words.

~~tr~~ fl gr	st gr fr
ip	ill

trip

• Circle the noun in the sentence that matches the picture.

1. He has the (brush) in his hand.

2. He hit the big drum.

3. Josh got in the tub.

• Fill in the blank with the word from the Word Box that fits the pattern.

trash	rash	splash
brush	rush	_____
tub	rub	_____
fish	dish	_____

Word Box

wish

mush

~~splash~~

scrub

• Circle the words where the *y* ending makes the *e* sound.

1. I'm (Lizzy) the fuzzy bee.

2. Bossy will get dizzy.

3. Fuzzy Lizzy went buzzing by Snappy.

• Special names for something or someone are called proper nouns. Proper nouns begin with a capital letter. Write the words from the list under the right group.

Gus Tabby dog cat Bossy cow

nouns	proper nouns
cat	Tabby

• Lizzy the Bee (18)

• Cross out the letters that don't belong and write the word.

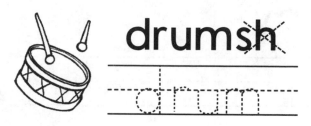 drumsh
~~drum~~

 sktruck
_____

 flpump
_____

 brushlk
_____

• Choose the correct word to complete the sentence.

Lizzy   lizzy

1. _Lizzy_ the bee can buzz.

tabby   Tabby

2. I will buzz by _____ the cat.

Bossy   bossy

3. _____ the cow will get dizzy.

• Write the sentences correctly.

1. kath is happy

Kath

2. is that mr tubbs

• Color all the words that end with *-uck* and *-ump* purple.
  Color all the words that have *-th* yellow.

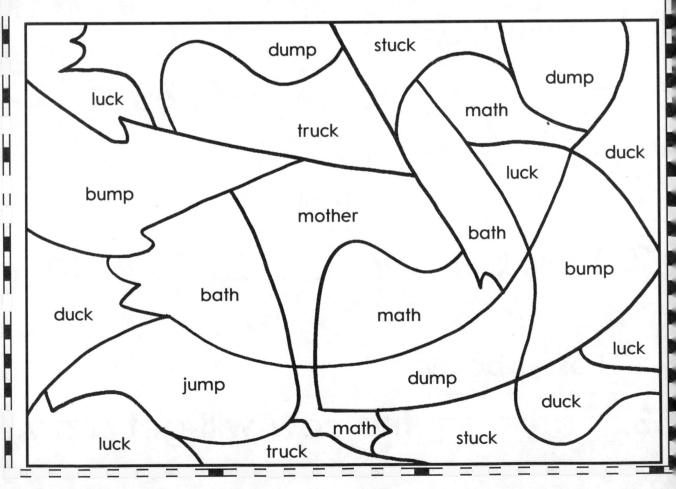

• Thump, Bump! (20)

• Put the correct punctuation mark at the end of each sentence.

1. Can the sleds go up the hill ☐

2. The sleds can go far ☐

3. What a day ☐

4. Are they going to stop ☐

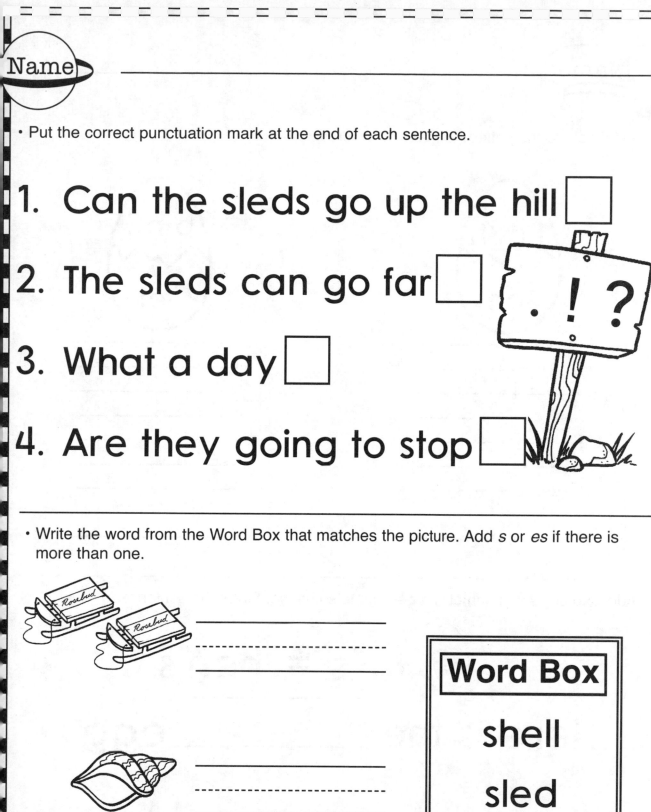

• Write the word from the Word Box that matches the picture. Add *s* or *es* if there is more than one.

_____

_____

_____

Word Box

shell

sled

box

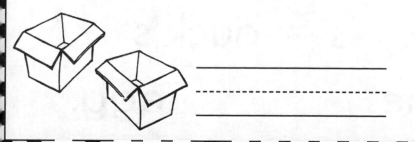

• Add letters to the pattern to make new words.

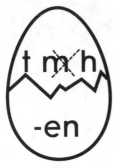

• Add 's to show that something belongs to someone. Finish the sentences.

hen + 's = hen's

Here is the _____ egg.

duck + 's = duck's

Here is the _____ egg.

• Words that show more than one are called plurals. Circle the plural words.
  Then write them.

The camp has ten (tents) *tents*

The eggs are in the grass. _____

The sleds are fast! _____

• Write the words from the list under the right group.

~~tent~~ sleds pet nest eggs ~~legs~~

one	more than one
tent	*legs*

303

• Write the word. Then draw a line to the picture in the box that rhymes with the word.

_____

_____

_____

• Find all the words in the Word Box that are hidden in the big square. Circle the words as you find them. They can be read across ➞ or down ↓.

a	b	t	h	a	n	k
y	e	d	u	t	e	o
e	g	s	k	a	w	l
s	o	m	e	p	i	r
r	o	h	g	w	e	h
t	d	o	e	s	l	o
b	c	x	d	p	i	w

Word Box

some

does

~~how~~

good

thank

new

• Chet and Chuck (24)

• Write the sentences correctly.

1. what do i spy

What

2. i spy a sly fox

• Color the words that end with -y brown. Color the words that end with -ch and -tch green.

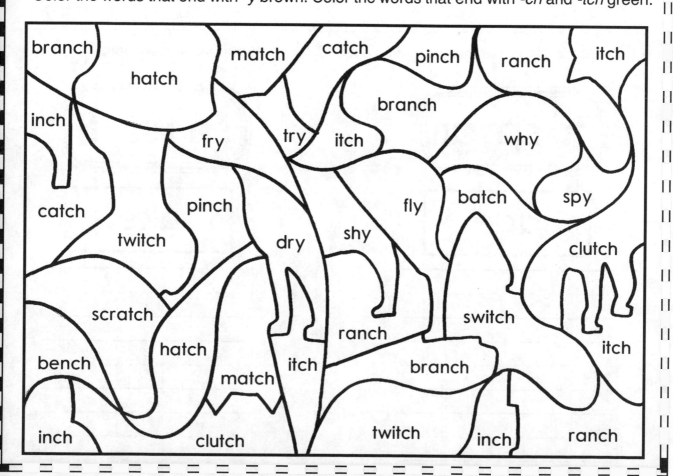

branch, match, catch, pinch, ranch, itch, hatch, branch, inch, fry, try, itch, why, catch, pinch, fly, batch, spy, twitch, dry, shy, clutch, scratch, switch, hatch, ranch, itch, bench, match, itch, branch, inch, clutch, twitch, inch, ranch

Name _____

• Write the beginning blend for each picture. You will need to write more than one letter.

‑‑‑‑‑‑‑‑‑‑‑‑‑‑‑‑

s n

‑‑‑‑‑‑‑‑‑‑‑‑‑‑‑‑

‑‑‑‑‑‑‑‑‑‑‑‑‑‑‑‑

‑‑‑‑‑‑‑‑‑‑‑‑‑‑‑‑

‑‑‑‑‑‑‑‑‑‑‑‑‑‑‑‑

‑‑‑‑‑‑‑‑‑‑‑‑‑‑‑‑

‑‑‑‑‑‑‑‑‑‑‑‑‑‑‑‑

• Look at the pattern in the box. Add blends to the pattern to make new words.

tr sp gr

ade

‑‑‑‑‑‑‑‑‑‑‑‑‑‑‑‑‑‑‑‑‑‑

‑‑‑‑‑‑‑‑‑‑‑‑‑‑‑‑‑‑‑‑‑‑

‑‑‑‑‑‑‑‑‑‑‑‑‑‑‑‑‑‑‑‑‑‑

‑‑‑‑‑‑‑‑‑‑‑‑‑‑‑‑‑‑‑‑‑‑

sn st fl

ake

‑‑‑‑‑‑‑‑‑‑‑‑‑‑‑‑‑‑‑‑‑‑

‑‑‑‑‑‑‑‑‑‑‑‑‑‑‑‑‑‑‑‑‑‑

‑‑‑‑‑‑‑‑‑‑‑‑‑‑‑‑‑‑‑‑‑‑

‑‑‑‑‑‑‑‑‑‑‑‑‑‑‑‑‑‑‑‑‑‑

• Can We Still Be Friends? (26)

Name _____

• Write the word for each picture. Add *s* or *es* if there is more than one.

_____

- -

_____

_____

- -

_____

_____

- -

_____

_____

- -

_____

• Add *'s* to show that something belongs to someone.

Grandpa + 's hens
_____
- hens
_____

Dane + 's skates
_____
- skates
_____

• Cross out the letters that don't belong and write the word.

 wavesh
_____
- - - - - - - - - - -
_____

thsquare
_____
- - - - - - - - - - -

 brspade
_____
- - - - - - - - - - -

snakech
_____
- - - - - - - - - - -

 gameck
_____
- - - - - - - - - - -

drplane
_____
- - - - - - - - - - -

• Put the correct punctuation mark at the end of each sentence.

1. Look out for that tree ☐

2. They are brave ☐

3. Can Jane skate ☐

4. Dave is waving ☐

5. Hold on ☐

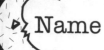

• Write the sentences correctly.

1.   the mans face is cold

The

2.   he is on the planes wing

_____

_____

• Color all the words that end with *-ace* and *-ave* blue.
  Color all the words that end with *-ane* and *-ate* brown.

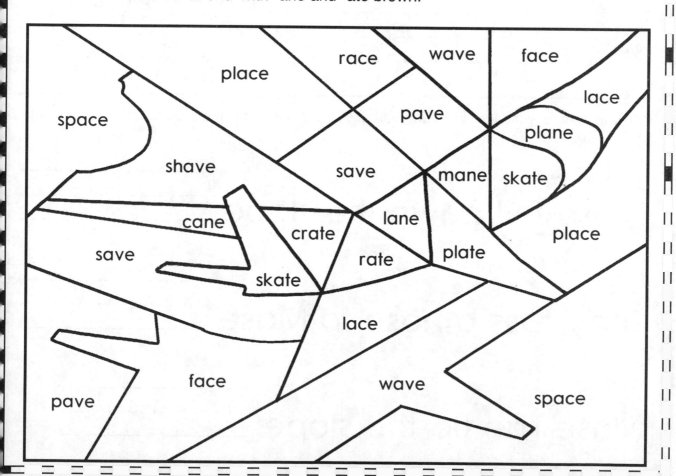

Name _____

• Write the word. Then draw a line to the picture in the box that rhymes with the word.

 _____

 _____

GUM _____

• Words that show action are called verbs. Circle the verbs in the sentences and then write the verbs.

Mose (fell) down the slope. _fell___

They toss a hose to Mose. _____

Mose ran up the slope. _____

• Write the words from the list under the right group.

smell pole run nose hit rope

nouns	verbs
pole	smell

• Find all the words in the Word Box that are hidden in the big square. Circle the words as you find them. They can be read across ⟶ or down ↓ .

w	o	u	l	d	o	p
h	e	t	o	r	b	u
e	n	d	y	m	s	l
r	a	s	m	a	l	l
e	j	w	e	n	d	o
l	f	s	i	y	a	n
r	c	o	l	d	t	x

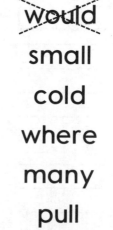

Word Box

would

small

cold

where

many

pull

• Words that show action are called verbs. Choose the verb from each list and write it in each sentence.

1. Cole _____ down the pole.

| big |
| slid |
| nose |

2. I can _____ the note.

| read |
| Sam |
| shell |

3. Max and Sam _____ a stone.

| bed |
| fast |
| see |

_____

• Look at the pattern in the box. Add letters to the pattern to make new words.

sl h sc

sm ch j

st b c

| ope |

| oke |

| one |

_____ _____ _____

_____ _____ _____

_____ _____ _____

• Write the sentences correctly.

1. max sees a stone

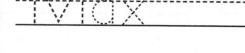
Max _____

_____

2. where is mose

_____

- -

_____

• Color the nouns green. Color the verbs red.

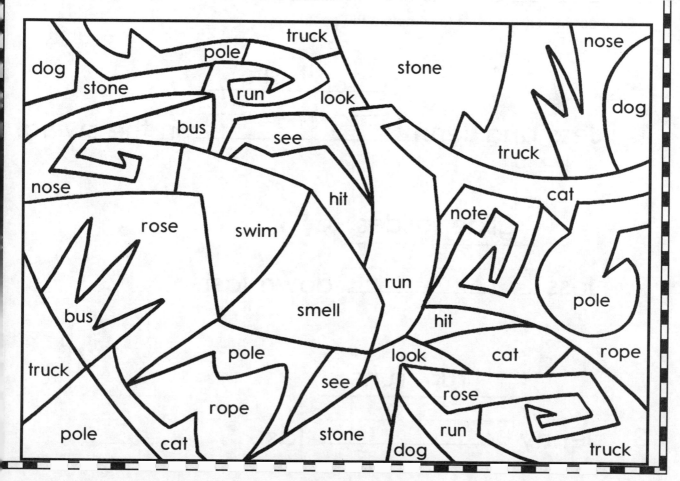

• Unscramble the word and write it.

 **orest**

store

 **idesl**

_____

 **imed**

_____

onest

_____

• Choose the correct word to complete the sentence.

sit   sits

1. Jess and Jenny ____sit____ in the swing.

glide glides

2. Jess _____ down fast.

run runs

3. Jenny _____ fast.

• Verbs that end in *-ed* tell about actions that have already happened. Write the words from the list under the right group.

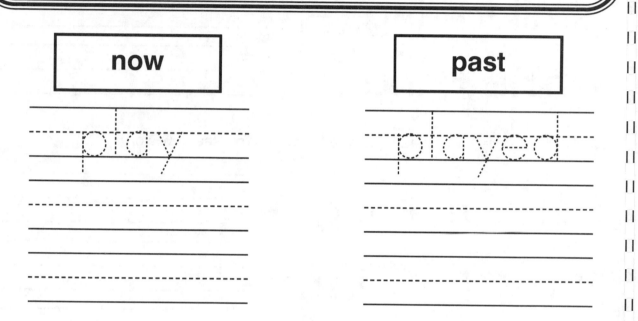

~~play~~   shined   whine   ~~played~~   whined   shine

now	past
play	played

• Write the verb. Add *-ed* to the verb to show that it has already happened.

He (play) _played_ at the park.

Jenny (look) _____ for Jess.

The wind (start) _____ to blow.

• Drop the silent *e* and add *-ing* to each verb. Write the new word.

slide + ing = _sliding_

smile + ing = _____

whine + ing = _____

• Double the last letter and add *-ing* to each verb. Write the new word.

run + n + ing = _running_

stop + p + ing = _____

sit + t + ing = _____

• Put the correct punctuation mark at the end of each sentence.

1. I can see you ☐

2. The sun shines ☐

3. Why are you sad ☐

4. What a fun day ☐

Name _____

• Write the sentences correctly.

1.   why are you sad

W̲h̲y̲

2.   what a happy bunch

_____

_____

_____

• Color the words that end with *-ine* green.
  Color the words that end with *-ice* and *-ive* yellow.

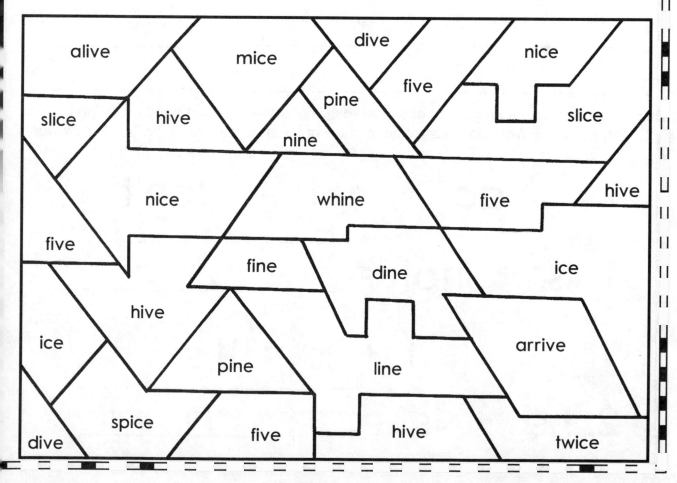

alive   mice   dive   nice
slice   hive   pine   five   slice
        nine
nice   whine   five   hive
five   fine   dine   ice
hive   arrive
ice   pine   line
spice   five   hive   twice
dive

Name _____

• Write each word on the list below the matching pattern.

pine ~~cute~~ flute five drive dine hive jute fine

ute	ive	ine
cute		

• A contraction is a short form of two words. Shorten the second word by taking out one or two letters. Write an apostrophe in place of the missing letters. Write the new word.

do + not = don't

1. is + not = _____

it + is = it's

2. he + is = _____

• Brute and the Flute (38

Name _____

• Make a contraction by combining the two words. Shorten the second word by taking out one or two letters. Write an apostrophe in place of the missing letter. Write the new word.

she + will = _she'll_

we + will = _____

was + not = _____

does + not = _____

she + is = _____

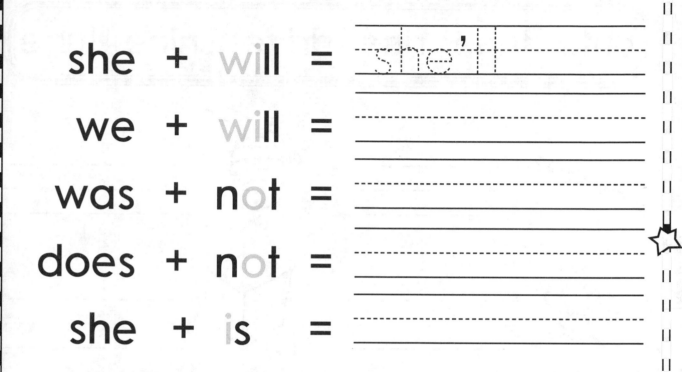

• Find all the words in the Word Box that are hidden in the big square. Circle the words as you find them. They can be read across ⟶ or down ↓.

c	k	n	o	w	h	i
r	a	h	j	o	l	d
e	t	a	f	r	a	m
t	h	i	n	k	u	v
w	e	g	o	s	h	e
a	r	o	u	n	d	r
b	e	u	r	o	k	y

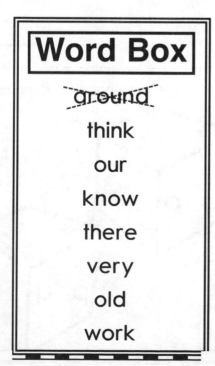

Word Box

~~around~~

think

our

know

there

very

old

work

319   • Old Rosa (39)

- Write the word from the list that rhymes with the picture.

cute tune rice drive shine tube

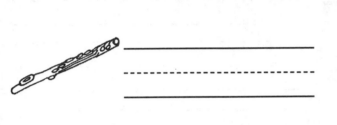

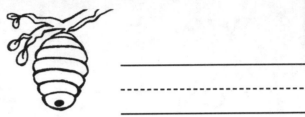

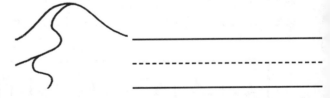

- Write the missing letter to complete the ABC pattern.

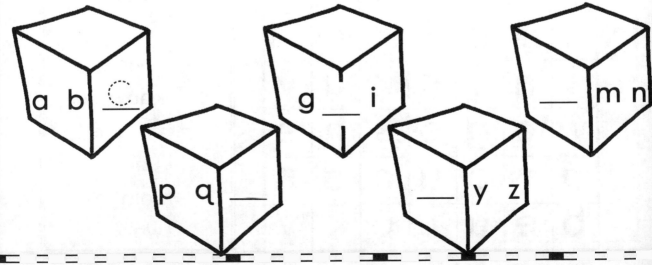

a b __   g __ i   __ m n

p q __   __ y z

- What Is in the Tree? (4

• Write the sentences correctly.

1.   its fluffy the cat

It's _____

_____

2.   dont i look cute

_____

_____

_____

• Color the contractions black.
  Color the words that end with -*ute*, -*ube*, -*une*, and -*ed* orange.

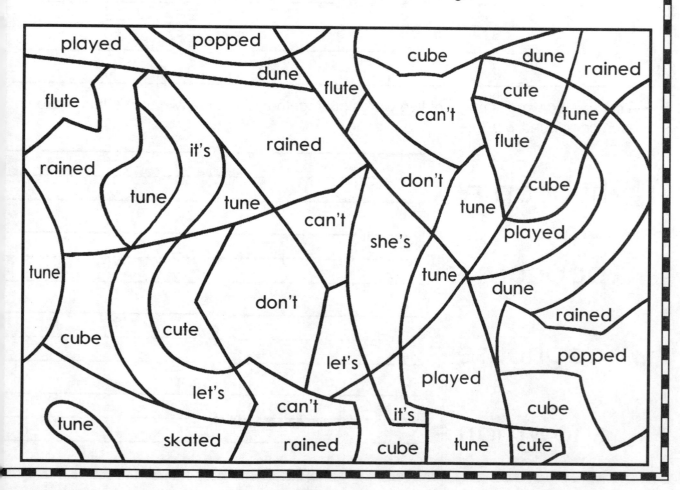

Name _____

• Write each word from the list below the matching pattern.

speed feet jeep need street keep steep

eed	eep	eet

• A compound word is made of two words put together. Write the two words that make up each compound word.

 hubcap = 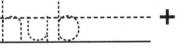 hub + 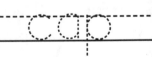 cap

 popcorn = _____ + _____

🏠 **doghouse** = _____ + _____

⛄ **snowman** = _____ + _____

Name _____

• Choose two words from the list that make a compound word. Write the new word.

cup   sand   foot   cow   star   lip

ball   fish   cake   box   stick   boy

lipstick

_____

• Find all the words in the Word Box that are hidden in the big square. Circle the words as you find them. They can be read across ⟶ or down ↓ .

o	n	l	y	b	u	n
p	t	e	v	e	r	y
u	s	m	o	g	n	o
s	h	o	w	a	b	t
h	g	l	a	n	r	h
e	z	k	i	d	s	e
o	b	e	t	t	e	r

Word Box

~~every~~

show

push

only

wait

other

better

began

323   • Sammy and Pete (43)

Name _____

• Write the word from the list that rhymes with the picture.

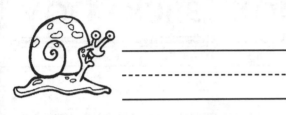

meal   dream   leak   nail   keep   rain

 _____

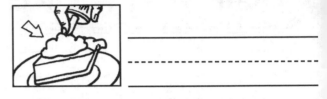 _____

_____

_____

 _____

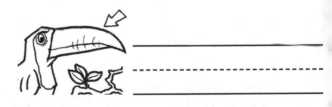 _____

• Words that tell more about nouns are called adjectives. Fill in the blank with an adjective from the Word Box.

The _____ snail saw a trail.

The _____ puppy hurt his tail.

My _____ jeep can go fast.

Word Box

gray

green

little

Name

• Write the sentences correctly.

1. im so glad i came

I'm

2. will you play with me

• Color the words that end with *-ute, -eed, -eep* and *-une* yellow.
Color the compound words pink.

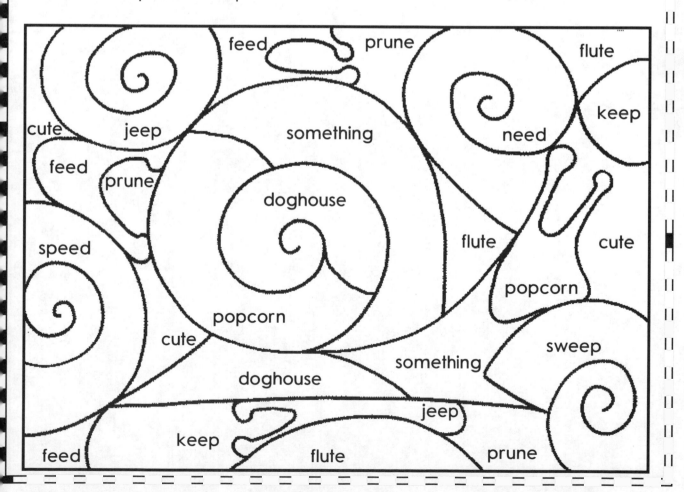

feed prune flute

cute jeep something need keep

feed prune doghouse

speed flute cute

popcorn

popcorn

cute doghouse something sweep

doghouse jeep

feed keep flute prune

325

SECTION O

NEWSLETTERS

HOME LINK NEWSLETTERS

HOME LINK

N E W S L E T T E R

Dear Parent,

During the coming year, your child will be using *Level Two* of the *Waterford Early Reading Program*. This program is based on interactive computer instruction and is designed to help your child gain important reading skills at his or her own pace. The activities in *Level Two* include games, exercises, and books that focus on the skills listed below.

- Word recognition
- Comprehension
- Phonological awareness
- Letter sound knowledge
- Spelling
- Writing

Throughout the school year, your child will be bringing home several books to add to his or her personal library. These books include 53 Readables that your child can read independently and 16 Traditional Tales that you can read together. There are also 22 Read-Along Books that are available from the class library.

Even though your child will gain many skills on the computer and in the classroom, he or she will benefit greatly from your support and encouragement at home. Periodically you will receive a newsletter to keep you informed of the skills your child is learning. Each newsletter will suggest ways for you to help him or her practice these skills.

Here are some general guidelines for helping your child gain as much as possible from the *Level Two* books and computer activities:

- **Be positive about accomplishments.** What your child is doing may seem simple or elementary to you, but it is actually a big step in intellectual and emotional development. Praise your child often and accept his or her efforts.
- **Schedule time for reading every day.** Read a variety of books with your child each day, including the Readables, Read-Along Books, and Traditional Tales from the *Waterford Early Reading Program*.
- **Visit the library regularly.** Borrow books from the library that you and your child can share together.
- **As you read, explain what words mean.** You may want to ask your child the meaning of a word to see if your child knows it. Involve your child in the story by asking what will happen next or what he or she thinks about the ending.

Remember that your child learns best in short, relaxed activities that both of you enjoy. I hope that you will find these suggestions helpful. If you have any questions or concerns, please contact me.

Sincerely,

HOME LINK

NEWSLETTER

Welcome! This newsletter can help you make a difference in your child's education by connecting what he or she learns at school with activities at home. Doing educational activities with your child can help him or her become an able reader and writer.

In class during the next few weeks, your child will review the sounds and letters of the alphabet and learn to recognize some Power Words. (Power Words are sight words, the words that appear most frequently in printed text and that are difficult to sound out.)

1 SKILLS

Help your child practice the capital and lowercase letters of the alphabet. For example, you can let your child write the letters in different sizes and colors and with different writing tools. Have your child find the letters in newspapers or books. When you go shopping, help your child find the letters on food labels, in the store, or on street signs.

Aa, Bb, Cc, Dd, Ee, Ff, Gg, Hh, Ii, Jj, Kk, Ll, Mm, Nn, Oo, Pp, Qq, Rr, Ss, Tt, Uu, Vv, Ww, Xx, Yy, Zz

Write each Power Word listed below on a 3-by-5-inch card. Create **Bingo** cards with the Power Words written in a grid. Provide game markers and play **Bingo** with the Power Words until your child can recognize the words instantly.

a, it, is, on, me, the, what, in

Clap the names of members in your family to show the number of syllables in the name. For example:

You say: *Rus...ty*. Clap and say *Rus...ty*
Child says: Rus...ty (clapping on the syllables)

Put some objects on a table and have your child sort them according to beginning sounds.
For example, your child could group *pen*, *paper*, and *paste* together, or *spoon*, *scissors*, and *socks* together. Say the names of each object so that your child hears that the beginning sounds are the same.

2 READING

Your child will receive three Power Word Readables to add to his or her personal library. Encourage your child to read each story to you and then retell the story.
• *Me*
• *The Snowman*
• *The Mitten*

Your child will also receive a Traditional Tale. Share this story with your child by reading it aloud.
• *The Gingerbread Man*

3 WRITING

Make a file called "My Portfolio" for your child's personal writing or pictures. Let your child decorate the file and label it with his or her name.

Make writing a daily routine. Two activities your child can do every day are drawing pictures and writing about them or thinking about ideas and writing them down.

Help your child make an *I'm Glad I'm Me* story. Fold several pages of art paper in half and staple them in the center. Have your child write "I'm Glad I'm Me" on the cover. Then let your child draw and write what personal qualities he or she likes. Some ideas are: *I like to draw*, *I have good friends*, *I have a nice smile*, and so on.

This newsletter provides more ideas for educational activities that you and your child can do together. Try some of the suggestions to encourage reading and writing at home.

In Unit 1 your child will learn the letter sound /a/ as in *apple*, several new Power Words, and several new word patterns.

1 SKILLS

Review the capital and lowercase letters of the alphabet. Help your child practice writing the letters in salt, sugar, sand, or shaving foam.

Write each Power Word listed below on two 3-by-5-inch cards to make a matching pair. Then have your child play a memory matching game like **Concentration**. Turn all of the cards facedown and let your child try to find the matching pairs of words.

I, see, he, said, say, are, have, my

Have your child build real and nonsense words from the word patterns listed below. For example, your child can use the word pattern *-am* to make the words *bam, cam, gam, ham, jam, yam, clam, sham,* and *wham*. You may also want to have your child practice writing the word patterns only, which can improve his or her spelling skills.

-am, -ad, -at, -an, -and, -ap, -amp

Play a rhyming riddle game. For example:

You say:	What word rhymes with *sat* and
	starts with /b/? (the sound of *B*)
Child says:	bat
You say:	What word rhymes with *fun* and
	starts with /s/?
Child says:	sun

Play a **Secret Code** game with your child. Say words that are broken into parts and have your child tell you the whole word. For example:

You say:	bed...room. What is the word?
Child says:	bedroom
You say:	kit.. chen. What is the word?
Child says:	kitchen

2 READING

Your child will be bringing home several Readables to add to his or her personal library. Encourage your child to read each story to you and then retell the story.

• *I Am Sam*	• *What Is It?*
• *What Am I?*	• *Dan and Mac*
• *Sad Sam*	• *What a Band!*
• *Dad's Surprise*	• *Pat Can Camp*
• *Tad*	• *The Rabbit and the Turtle*
• *Matt's Hat*	

Your child will also receive two Traditional Tales. Share these stories with your child by reading them aloud.

• *The Little Red Hen*
• *Lizard and the Painted Rock*

The following Read-Along Books are available in the class library.

| • *Mine* | • *José Three* |

3 WRITING

Help your child make a book titled *I Can* or *I Like*. Your child can write or dictate sentences that describe favorite activities and then draw pictures to match the text.

Help your child write the recipe for a favorite food. The quantities and ingredients may not be accurate, but the recipe will be a fun item for your child's writing portfolio.

Let your child write signs to display in a room. Some ideas for signs are: *Stop!*; *Wash Your Hands*; *Kid's Crossing*; *Keep Out*; *Traffic Zone*; *Danger, Do Not Enter*; *Shhh, People Sleeping*; or *My Bedroom*.

HOME LINK

UNIT 2 · NEWSLETTER

As you complete these newsletter activities with your child, remember to provide genuine encouragement and give praise for even the smallest accomplishments.

In Unit 2 your child will learn the letter sound /o/ as in *octopus*, several new Power Words, and several new word patterns.

1 SKILLS

Write each Power Word listed below on several 3-by-5-inch cards. Then place the cards faceup and have your child play **Word Slap**. When you call out a Power Word, your child should "slap" each card that shows the word. Each correct slap allows your child to add the card to the "Words I Know" pile.

will, go, his, has, for, you, with, here

Have your child build real and nonsense words from the word patterns listed below. For example, your child can use the word pattern *-od* to make the words *bod, cod, dod, fod, mod, sod, tod, plod,* and *clod*. You may also want to have your child practice writing the word patterns only, which can improve his or her spelling skills.

-od, -ot, -op, -ob, -ab, -oss, -ox, -ax, -og, -ag

Have your child listen to groups of words and tell you which word doesn't rhyme with the others. Use the word groups below to begin.

    am...Sam...see...ram
    fun...mad...dad...had
    cop...can...stop...hop
    rod...map...Todd...nod

Play **Red Light, Green Light** with letter sounds. Choose a leader and a particular beginning or ending letter sound (such as /d/ as in *bad*). Then have the leader call out words while the remaining players walk forward. As long as the given word has the chosen sound in the correct position of the word (such as *old, red,* or *lid*), the players can walk forward. If the leader calls out a word that does not contain the letter sound (such as *lock*), the players must stop walking. Any players who continue walking when the "red light" signal is given must return to the starting line. The first player to reach the leader becomes the new leader.

2 READING

Your child will receive several Readables to add to his or her personal library. Encourage your child to read each story to you and then retell the story.

- *Stop the Frogs!*
- *Bob and Tab*
- *Hot Rods*
- *Happy Birthday*
- *Go, Frog Go!*

Your child will also receive a Traditional Tale. Share this story with your child by reading it aloud.
- *Anansi and the Seven Yam Hills*

The following Read-Along Books are available in the class library.
- *My Super Sticky Sandwich*
- *Ooey, Gooey Mud!*

3 WRITING

Help your child make a *Five Senses* book. Your child can write sentences that describe what he or she can smell, taste, hear, see, and feel. Then your child can cut out pictures from magazines to illustrate the sentences.

Let your child help you write a shopping list before you go to the store. Then your child can check off each item as it is put into the shopping cart.

Write small stories with your child about feelings. For example, your child can write sentences like
I am happy when _____,
I am sad when _____,
or I am angry when _____.

his newsletter and your involvement in your child's learning can help improve his or her reading and writing skills.

n Unit 3 your child will learn the letter sound /i/ as in *iguana*, several new Power Words, and several new word patterns.

1 SKILLS

Write each Power Word listed below on a separate 3-by-5-inch card. Then place the cards faceup and have your child play **Word Toss**. When you call out a Power Word, your child should toss a beanbag to each card that shows the word. Each correct toss allows your child to add the card to the "Words I Know" pile.

of, to, be, put, they she, her, from, who, come, let, your, we, too, yes, no

Have your child build real and nonsense words from the word patterns listed below. For example, your child can use the word pattern *-ip* to make the words *bip, dip, kip, rip, tip, vip, slip, whip,* and *chip*. You may also want to have your child practice writing the word patterns only, which can improve his or her spelling skills.

-ip, -ig, -in, -im, -id, -it, -ill, -int, -ing, -ack, -ock, -ick, -ash, -ish

Create a new language with your child. For example, you can change the beginning sound of a word to make a silly word: *carrot* becomes *barrot, bread* becomes *shread, watermelon* becomes *patermelon,* and so on.

Play **I'm Thinking of Something** while you ride together in the car. Make up riddles and have your child guess the word. For example:

> You say: I'm thinking of something that children like to ride. It begins with the /b/ sound. What is it?
>
> Child says: bike

2 READING

Your child will receive several Readables to add to his or her personal library. Encourage your child to read each story to you and then retell the story.
- *Pip, the Big Pig*   • *The Big Trip*
- *What Is in the Pit?*   • *Who Will Go in the Rain?*
- *Prints!*   • *Let's Get Hats!*
- *Who Is at the Door?*

Your child will also receive two Traditional Tales. Share these stories with your child by reading them aloud.
- *The Big Mitten*
- *The Three Little Pigs*

The following Read-Along Books are available in the class library.
- *Fawn Eyes*   • *Garden Visitors*
- *Little Monkey*

3 WRITING

Have your child create a *Pet Care* book. Your child can write questions about caring for an actual or imaginary pet. Then visit the library or a veterinarian together to find out the answers.

Take a walk in your neighborhood and have your child make a graph of the animals that live in the area.

Have your child make an *Animal Sounds* book. Your child can cut out pictures of animals from magazines and write a caption under each picture like *A cat meows, A cow moos,* and so on. At the end of the book, you may want to help your child draw a self-portrait and write the sentence *But I can talk.*

HOME LINK

UNIT 4 NEWSLETTER

Remember that your child learns best in short, relaxed activities that both of you enjoy. Try some of the suggestions in this newsletter to keep reading and writing meaningful for your child.

In Unit 4 your child will learn the letter sound /u/ as in *umbrella*, several new Power Words, and several new word patterns.

1 SKILLS

Write each Power Word listed below on a separate 3-by-5-inch card. Then hide the cards in a room and have your child play **Word Hunt**. When you call out a Power Word, your child should hunt for the matching card until he or she finds it. (If your child finds a Power Word that doesn't match what you said, he or she should leave the card in its hiding place.) Each correct match allows your child to add the card to the "Words I Know" pile.

now, look, down, went, then, get, that, by, little, so, like, why, do, mother, father, want, Mr.

Have your child build real and nonsense words from the word patterns listed below. For example, your child can use the word pattern *-ug* to make the words *dug, hug, jug, mug, tug, zug, chug, thug,* and *slug.* You may also want to have your child practice writing the word patterns.

-ug, -un, -ut, -um, -ub, -ush, -uzz, -izz, -uck, -uff, -ump

After going on an outing with your child, play a game about what you saw. Give the beginning sound of a word and have your child guess the word.

You say:	At the zoo, we saw a /l/...
Child says:	lion, leopard (and so on)
You say:	Then we saw a /z/...
Child says:	zebra

Play **Odd Man Out** with your child. Say some words and have your child give a signal such as a hand clap when he or she hears a word that has a different beginning sound. For example, you can focus on the sound /p/ and say words such as *pie, pink, purple, mouse, planet, pan, sand,* and so on. Later change the game by focusing on ending letter sounds or rhyming words.

2 READING

Your child will receive several Readables to add to his or her personal library. Encourage your child to read each story to you and then retell the story.
- *Slug Bug*
- *Green Gum*
- *Lizzy the Bee*
- *Little Duck*
- *Thump, Bump!*
- *The Tree Hut*

Your child will also receive a Traditional Tale. Share this story with your child by reading it aloud.
- *The City Mouse and the Country Mouse*

The following Read-Along Books are available in the class library.
- *The Alligator in the Library*
- *Story in the Snow*
- *Shell Houses*

3 WRITING

Help your child write riddles for different animals. For example, for a raccoon you could write, *I am brown, black, and white. I wear a mask. What am I?* Let your child draw pictures to match each riddle.

Have your child make animal puppets by cutting out pictures of animals from magazines and gluing the pictures to sticks. Then help your child write a play for the puppets. If your child wishes, he or she can present the play to friends or family members.

Visit a place such as the zoo, circus, farm, or aquarium. While you are there, have your child make a list of the animals he or she sees. Later your child can make a book about each trip, such as *My Zoo Animals* book, *My Circus Animals* book, and so on.

This newsletter provides more ideas for educational activities that you and your child can do together.

In Unit 5 your child will learn the letter sound /e/ as in *Ed*, several new Power Words, and several new word patterns.

1 SKILLS

Write each Power Word listed below on a 3-by-5-inch card. Create **Bingo** cards with the Power Words written in a grid. Provide game markers and play **Bingo** with the Power Words until your child can recognize the words instantly.

was, far, fall, day, out, or, find,
one, friend, new, tree, some, thank,
house, good, how, all, does

Have your child build real and nonsense words from the word patterns listed below. For example, your child can use the word pattern *-ed* to make the words *fed, jed, med, ped, red, wed, yed, sled,* and *shed*. You may also want to have your child practice writing the word patterns only, which can improve his or her spelling skills.

-ed, -ell, -est, -en, -et, -end,
-ent, -y (as in fly)

Play a **Secret Code** game with your child. Say words that are broken into two parts and have your child tell you the whole word. For example:

You say:	It is time to eat break...fast. What is it time for?
Child says:	breakfast
You say:	I see a pretty butter...fly. What do I see?
Child says:	butterfly

As you serve lunch or dinner to your child, mention what you are serving but leave off the beginning consonant. For example:

You say:	I'm hungry. Let's eat a _ickle. What is the word?
Child says:	pickle
You say:	What sound was missing?
Child says:	/p/

2 READING

Your child will receive several Readables to add to his or her personal library. Encourage your child to read each story to you and then retell the story.
- *The Big Hill*
- *What's in the Egg?*
- *Rom and His New Pet*
- *Chet and Chuck*
- *What Do I Spy?*
- *Quick! Help!*

Your child will also receive two Traditional Tales. Share these stories with your child by reading them aloud.
- *Goldilocks and the Three Bears*
- *The Magic Porridge Pot*

The following Read-Along Books are available in the class library.
- *Lost Socks*
- *Lumpy Mush*

3 WRITING

Help your child write a list of what he or she does each day. The list could include *get out of bed, eat breakfast, brush my teeth,* and so on.

Collect photographs of your child and arrange them in a photo album. Help your child write captions under each picture.

Have your child write about his or her favorite things such as a color, a sound, a place, a dream, a taste, a smell, or a time of day.

HOME LINK

UNIT 6 · NEWSLETTER

As you complete these newsletter activities with your child, remember to provide genuine encouragement and give praise for even the smallest accomplishments.

In Unit 6 your child will learn the letter sound /ā/ as in *race*, several new Power Words, and several new word patterns.

1 SKILLS

Write each Power Word listed below on two 3-by-5-inch cards to make a matching pair. Then have your child play a memory matching game like **Concentration**. Turn all of the cards facedown and let your child try to find the matching pairs of words.

play, were, sure, could, their, many, love, walk, hold, pull, cold, eyes, ears

Have your child build real and nonsense words from the word patterns listed below. For example, your child can use the word pattern *-ade* to make the words *bade, fade, lade, made, tade, wade, trade, shade, and blade*. You may also want to have your child practice writing the word patterns only, which can improve his or her spelling skills.

-ade, -ake, -ame, -ane, -ate, -ave, -are, -ace, -age

Play a rhyming riddle game. For example:

    You say: What word rhymes with rope and
                  starts with /s/?
    Child says: soap

Continue the game with these words and new letter sounds:

    twister.../s/
    store.../d/
    mountain.../f/
    flipper.../z/
    flower.../p/
    school.../p/

Play a **Secret Code** game with your child. Say words that are broken into parts and have your child tell you the whole word. For example:

    You say: bi...g. What is the word?
    Child says: big
    You say: foo...t. What is the word?
    Child says: foot
Continue the game with other words.

2 READING

Your child will receive several Readables to add to his or her personal library. Encourage your child to read each story to you and then retell the story.
• *Can We Still Be Friends?*
• *Fun in Kansas*
• *Brave Dave and Jane*
• *My Snowman*
• *Space Chase Race*

Your child will also receive a Traditional Tale. Share this story with your child by reading it aloud.
• *The Three Wishes*

The following Read-Along Books are available in the class library.
• *The Germs*
• *The Swing*

3 WRITING

Have a **Storytelling Family Night**. Gather your family members together to tell stories. Discuss that a story has a beginning, middle, and end.

Write or discuss real and make-believe things with your child. For example, your child could write, *I see a cat and it is real*, or *I see a monster and it is not real*. The library is a wonderful place to find stories about real and make-believe events.

Have your child draw pictures of what they wish for and then write appropriate captions.

Your involvement in your child's learning will help improve his or her reading and writing skills.

In Unit 7 your child will learn the letter sound /ō/ as in *rope*, several new Power Words, and several new word patterns.

1 SKILLS

Write each Power Word listed below on several 3-by-5-inch cards. Then place the cards faceup and have your child play **Word Slap**. When you call out a Power Word, your child should "slap" each card that shows the word. Each correct slap allows your child to add the card to the "Words I Know" pile.

would, where, over, room, small, read, please, any, door, because, live

Have your child build real and nonsense words from the word patterns listed below. For example, your child can use the word pattern *-ope* to make the words *bope, cope, dope, hope, lope, mope, nope, rope,* and *slope*. You may also want to have your child practice writing the word patterns only, which can improve his or her spelling skills.

-ope, -ose, -oke, -ole, -one, -ode, -ote, -ore, -ove

Sing "A-Hunting We Will Go" with your child:
    A-hunting we will go,
    A-hunting we will go!
    We'll catch a fox
    And put him in a box,
    And then we'll let him go.
Change the words *fox* and *box* to other rhyming words, such as "We'll catch a *pig* and put him in a *rig*" or "We'll catch an *ape* and put him in a *grape*."

Play a **Secret Code** game with your child. Say words that are broken into parts and have your child tell you the whole word. For example:

You say:	I like to r...ea...d. What do I like to do?
Child says:	read
You say:	I can d...a...n...ce. What can I do?
Child says:	dance
You say:	My favorite color is y...e...ll...ow. What is my favorite color?
Child says:	yellow

2 READING

Your child will receive several Readables to add to his or her personal library. Encourage your child to read each story to you and then retell the story.
- *Oh No, Mose!*
- *Smoke!*
- *The Note*
- *The Snoring Boar*
- *Shopping Day*

Your child will also receive two Traditional Tales. Share these stories with your child by reading them aloud.
- *Henny Penny*
- *Mr. Lucky Straw*

The following Read-Along Books are available in the class library.
- *The Watermelon Seed*
- *Moon Song*

3 WRITING

Go on a nature walk with your child. Then have your child write about the walk in his or her journal.

Have your child create a book titled *My Seeds*. Help your child gather different types of seeds, tape the seeds to the pages of the book, and write appropriate captions.

Purchase flower or vegetable seeds and help your child plant the seeds in your yard or in a pot Your child can write about caring for the plants as they grow.

HOME LINK

UNIT 8 NEWSLETTER

Try some of the suggestions in this newsletter to keep reading and writing meaningful for your child.

In Unit 8 your child will learn the letter sound /T/ as in *time*, several new Power Words, and several new word patterns.

1 SKILLS

Write each Power Word listed below on a separate 3-by-5-inch card. Then place the cards faceup and have your child play **Word Toss**. When you call out a Power Word, your child should toss a beanbag to each card that shows the word. Each correct toss allows your child to add the card to the "Words I Know" pile.

> tomorrow, buy, two, start,
> school, don't, under, never, eat,
> our, there, know

Have your child build real and nonsense words from the word patterns listed below. For example, your child can use the word pattern *-ide* to make the words *bide, dide, hide, mide, side, glide, slide*, and *pride*. You may also want to have your child practice writing the word patterns only, which can improve his or her spelling skills.

> -ide, -ime, -ine, -ite, -ice,
> -ire, -ile, -ive, -ike, -ipe

Play **The Changing Word** with your child. Write a word on a piece of paper. (Or you may want to use magnetic letters.) Then show your child how changing one letter in the word can make a new word. For example, change:
slam to *slim* to *slip* to *flip* to *flop* to *flap* to *clap* to *clam*
top to *tip* to *rip* to *hip* to *hop* to *hope* to *slope* to *rope*
hat to *mat* to *mad* to *made* to *make* to *wake* to *woke*

Tell your child a familiar or traditional story, occasionally getting "stuck" on a word and saying only the letter sounds. (Choose words with five or fewer letter sounds.) Then have your child blend the sounds together and tell you the whole word before you continue the story. For example:

> You say: Once upon a time, there were three little p...i...g...s. What is the word?
> Child says: pigs

2 READING

Your child will receive several Readables to add to his or her personal library. Encourage your child to read each story to you and then retell the story.
• *Friends*
• *Two Little Pines*
• *Can Matilda Get the Cheese?*
• *Let's Go to Yellowstone*
• *Maddy and Clive*

Your child will also receive a Traditional Tale. Share this story with your child by reading it aloud.
• *La Tortuga*

The following Read-Along Books are available in the class library.
• *What Is a Cloud?*
• *Legs*

3 WRITING

Have your child make a list of "weather words" such as *sunny, rainy, hot, dry, snowy, windy,* and *cloudy*. Then help your child put the weather words on a graph and chart the weather daily. At the end of the month, your child can count the number of sunny days, rainy days, and so on.

Let your child keep a weather journal. For example, he or she could write *Today is windy. I will wear a jacket.*

Watch clouds with your child and help him or her look for familiar shapes such as animals or objects. Then have your child draw a picture of the imagined object and write a story about the cloud.

HOME LINK

UNIT 9 NEWSLETTER

Remember that your child learns best in short, relaxed activities that both of you enjoy.

In Unit 9 your child will learn the letter sound /u/ ās in *mute*, several new Power Words, and several new word patterns.

1 SKILLS

Write each Power Word listed below on a separate 3-by-5-inch card. Then hide the cards in a room and have your child play **Word Hunt**. When you call out a Power Word, your child should hunt for the matching card until he or she finds it. (If your child finds a Power Word that doesn't match what you said, he or she should leave the card in its hiding place.) Each correct match allows your child to add the card to the "Words I Know" pile.

around, think, very, old, work, every, way, saw, began, better

Have your child build real and nonsense words from the word patterns listed below. For example, your child can use the word pattern *-ute* to make the words *cute, jute, lute, mute, rute, tute, brute,* and *flute*. You may also want to have your child practice writing the word patterns only, which can improve his or her spelling skills.

-ute, -ude, -ube, -ule, -une, -use

Provide a piece of paper that is divided or creased into three equal sections. Also provide a place marker such as a penny. Say a word. Have your child decide whether a given sound is at the beginning, middle, or end of the word and place the marker in the appropriate section of the paper. For example:

You say: Kitten. Where do you hear the
             sound /t/?
Child says: In the middle (placing the marker
             in the middle section of the paper).

Say a name broken into two parts (the first sound and the rest of the word) and have your child tell you the whole name. For example:

You say: /b/...ob. Who is it?
Child says: Bob
You say: /ch/...andler. Who is it?
Child says: Chandler

2 READING

Your child will receive several Readables to add to his or her personal library. Encourage your child to read each story to you and then retell the story.
• *Brute and the Flute*
• *Old Rosa*
• *What Is in the Tree?*
• *Too Much Popcorn*
• *Old King Dune*

Your child will also receive two Traditional Tales. Share these stories with your child by reading them aloud.
• *The Shoemaker and the Elves*
• *The Brothers*

The following Read-Along Books are available in the class library.
• *In the Rain*
• *Moving Day*

3 WRITING

Help your child write and address a simple letter to a family member, friend, or community member. If your child receives a response, you can help him or her read the letter.

Let your child make birthday cards, banners, or letters to send to a family member, neighbor, or schoolmate.

Have your child write thank-you notes to someone special. Let your child design and create envelopes to go with the notes.

HOME LINK

UNIT 10 NEWSLETTER

In Unit 10 your child will learn the letter sounds /ē̄ē/ as in *feet* and *steam*, /ā/ as in *rain* and *stay*, and /ō/ as in *boat*. Your child will also learn to recognize several new Power Words and word patterns. As well as words that contain the word patterns.

1 SKILLS

Write each Power Word listed below on a 3-by-5-inch card. Create **Bingo** cards with the Power Words written in a grid. Provide game markers and play **Bingo** with the Power Words until your child can recognize the words instantly.

show, push, only, wait, other, thought, soon, after, laugh, both

Have your child build real and nonsense words from the word patterns listed below. For example, your child can use the word pattern *-eep* to make the words *beep, deep, heep, jeep, neep, weep, steep, sleep,* and *creep.* You may also want to have your child practice writing the word patterns only, which can improve his or her spelling skills.

-eep, -eed, -eet, -eak, -eal, -eam, -ail, -ain, -ay, -oat, -oad

Play a guessing game with your child. Say a word and ask what would be left if the first sound were deleted. Then have your child say the new word. For example:

You say: *Box.* What would be left if the first sound, /b/, were taken away?

Child says: ox

Continue playing this game, using these and other words:

wax, ax	cart, art
mad, ad	red, ed
lark, ark	pin, in

Play **The Changing Word** with your child. Write a word on a piece of paper. (Or you may want to use magnetic letters.) Then show your child how changing one letter in the word can make a new word. For example, change:

bit to *pit* to *pin* to *pine* to *nine* to *shine* to *vine*
hit to *bit* to *bite* to *white* to *quite* to *spite*
hit to *mit* to *mite* to *mice* to *nice* to *rice* to *spice*
ham to *jam* to *Jim* to *Tim* to *time* to *tire*

2 READING

Your child will receive several Readables to add to his or her personal library. Encourage your child to read each story to you and then retell the story.
• *Riding in My Jeep*
• *Sammy and Pete*
• *Will You Play with Me?*
• *The Rescue*
• *Who Am I?*

Your child will also receive a Traditional Tale. Share this story with your child by reading it aloud.
• *The Ugly Duckling*

The following Read-Along Books are available in the class library.
• *Seeing Fingers*
• *Play Ball*

3 WRITING

Make a *Friends* book with your child. Your child can write sentences that describe what he or she has done with a friend. For example: *On Monday, we went to the park. On Tuesday, we...*

Help your child and a group of friends write down ways that they can make your neighborhood a better place to visit. For example, they can clean up graffiti or trash, paint fences, plant flowers, sweep gutters, and so on. Enlist the help of other parents to carry out the ideas.

Help your child make a book titled *A Friend Is Someone Who...* Your child can write sentences that describe his or her idea of a true friend. Then your child can draw pictures to go with the text.